Teacher Key

ARITHMETIC 4

Tests and Speed Drills

A Beka Book®
— A MINISTRY OF —
PENSACOLA CHRISTIAN COLLEGE
PENSACOLA, FLORIDA 32523-9160

To the Teacher

The Student Tests and Speed Drills Book for *Arithmetic 4* includes sixteen biweekly tests, a final exam, sixteen bi-weekly quizzes and 136 speed drills (four per week). One copy of the book is needed for each student.

The Teacher Key has suggestions for administering, the answers, and a suggested scale for each test and quiz.

Speed Drills

Speed drills are given daily except for test or quiz days. **Each sheet contains one week's worth of speed drills.** Most teachers like to send the sheets home weekly to keep parents informed. Any speed drills that are not done in school can be completed at home.

The purposes of the speed drills are to give the students practice with their combinations and other memory work and to increase speed with all four processes. **The speed drills are timed, so students must know their combinations and other memory work well in order to finish.**

Most speed drills do not affect the students' grades and are most helpful when not used as competition among class members. Students should strive to improve their scores and to compete against their own scores.

Students who do poorly on the speed drills may need to attend Arithmetic Help Class.

Suggested procedure for administering the speed drills:

1. Hand out speed drills sheets to the students. On the first day of a new week, most teachers find it is a help to have them counted out by rows for quick distribution. Students should pass in the speed drills in order. Have the first student in each row criss-cross them so the speed drills are ready for quick distribution the following day.

2. Tell students to put their paper so the name and score side shows. If it is the first day on the speed drill sheet, students need to write their names. They should put their pencils down as soon as they have written their names.

3. Tell students which number speed drill they are to do for the day.

4. Tell students to pick up their pencils and to begin as soon as you tell them to. Tell them that as soon as you say *stop* that they should put their pencils down and stop even if they have not finished the speed drill. They should understand that one goal of arithmetic is to work quickly. Walk around the room to make sure students are answering the correct speed drill.

Third Edition

Copyright © 1995, 1991, 1980 Pensacola Christian College
All rights reserved. Printed in U.S.A. 2002/2 C00

5. Give students the **designated time** to complete the drill. Tell them to *stop* when time is up. The length of each speed drill is on the drills and in the *Curriculum/Lesson Plans*.

6. Have students put their pencils away and get out pens. Call out the answers and have students check their work. Often students can grade their own speed drills when the grades are not recorded. Checking their own drills helps them to see what they missed. The students should exchange and check all graded speed drills. Students enjoy the variety, and it gives them practice grading another paper. You can have the students write either the number wrong or the number right in the space provided on the name side of the drill.

7. Collect drills and briefly check over after school. Grades are recorded once each week. Both the *Teacher Tests and Speed Drills* and the *Curriculum/Lesson Plans* designate which speed drills are graded. There is room for a stamp or sticker next to the grade if a student made no mistakes or improved.

8. Send speed drills home after they are completed. A speed drill that was not done due to absence or lack of time can be completed at home by students if parents desire. It is not necessary for students to return the speed drills after showing to parents. Some parents like to display their child's speed drills on the refrigerator or other places in the home. Some teachers like to display speed drills around the room.

Quizzes

Quizzes are given biweekly and are comprehensive.

Suggested procedure for administering the bi-weekly quizzes:

1. Hand out quizzes while students get out a clean cover sheet and pencil. Most teachers find that it is a help if they count out the quizzes by rows for quick distribution.

2. Briefly look at the quiz together and answer the students questions about the instructions. Students should not ask questions about how to work problems or ask questions after the quiz begins. For the first quiz, explain and demonstrate how to use a cover sheet.

3. Give students 7–10 minutes to complete. If everyone finishes sooner, stop when all are finished. Train the students who finish before time is called to check answers carefully.

4. Exchange and grade. Students use a pen to grade. Call out the answers. Students draw a straight line through any wrong answers. Most teachers find that it is better not to tell students the value of each question. It is usually easier if the teacher figures the grade after school.

5. The grading goes much quicker and smoother if students are not allowed to ask questions during the grading of the quiz. If the student grading or the owner of the quiz has any questions, a question mark should be put at the top of the quiz and beside the answers that are in question.

6. Check over grading and determine the number of points missed. Subtract from 100 the points missed. Record the grade in the box provided at the top of quiz.

7. Record the grades and return the quiz the following day so the students can see the grade. Collect and keep the quizzes until the scheduled time to send them home to parents. Parents should return the quiz to you the day after receiving. Quizzes also make good papers to display in the classroom.

Tests

Tests are given biweekly and are comprehensive since arithmetic is a building-block subject.

Suggested procedure for administering the biweekly tests:

1. Students need a pencil and two clean sheets of paper. One sheet is a check sheet. Students who finish before time is called should be trained to write problems on the check sheet and to check answers carefully. The second sheet is for a cover sheet. You may want to supply the cover sheets. Hand out the cover sheets before the test and collect them after the test. The same cover sheets could be used for all tests. Distribute the tests to students. Most teachers find that it is a help if they count out the tests by rows for quick distribution.

2. Tell students to put their names and the date at the top of the test paper. They should then put down the pencil and wait for instructions.

3. Explain each section. Allow the students to ask questions about the directions but not about how to do the problems before the test begins. Students should not ask questions after the test begins. All students begin the test at the same time.

4. Walk around the room during the test to make sure the students are progressing at a reasonable rate and are using the cover sheets. If a student finishes the test before the time is called, he checks his work. When his test has been carefully checked, he reads quietly at his desk.

5. Teach the students how to pass in the tests when time is called. Many teachers find that it is a great help if they train their students to bring the tests to teacher's desk in alphabetical order. They put the tests face down. If you supplied the cover sheet, they put the cover sheets in a pile beside the test sheets. **The teacher grades all tests without any student help.** To get the number grade for the test, subtract the number of points missed from 100.

6. Have tests graded and ready to return to students as soon as possible. Students need to find what errors they are making and correct their thinking. Students should have nothing on their desks when tests are returned. They should look over the tests carefully and see what mistakes they made. If several students missed the same problem, you may want to work it on the chalkboard for the students. After students look over their tests, collect and keep them until the scheduled time to send tests home to parents. Parents should return them to you the day after receiving.

Lesson 2 — 3 min.

```
  7 3        3 9        6 8        4 5
+ 4 6      + 7 5      + 1 9      + 8 7
-----      -----      -----      -----
1 1 9      1 1 4        8 7      1 3 2


  9 8        6 8        1 8        2 9
+ 3 1      + 4 7      + 7 6      + 5 7
-----      -----      -----      -----
1 2 9      1 1 5        9 4        8 6


  4 7 2        3 2 7        6 5 8
+   8 9      + 9 1 4      + 4 9 5
-------      -------      -------
  5 6 1      1, 2 4 1      1, 1 5 3
```

Lesson 3 — 3 min.

```
                       9
  9 3      1 4 2       7      5 9 4
  8 7      6 8 7       8      6 7 2
  5 6      9 5 3       6      1 4 5
  2 9      2 4 7       3      8 7 2
+ 3 5    + 6 5 1     + 7    + 1 6 6
-----    -------     ---    -------
3 0 0    2, 6 8 0     4 0    2, 4 4 9


  6, 8 7 5      2, 9 4 1      $ 1 6 . 7 2
+ 9, 3 2 1    + 8, 1 6 7    + 4 3 . 3 7
---------     ---------     -----------
1 6, 1 9 6    1 1, 1 0 8     $ 6 0 . 0 9
```

Lesson 4 — 3 min.

$4 + 9 + 6 + 7 + 3 + 2 =$ __31__

$11 + 5 + 6 + 3 + 8 + 7 =$ __40__

$9 + 0 + 3 + 1 + 8 + 2 =$ __23__

$6 + 9 + 5 + 8 + 2 + 3 =$ __33__

$5 + 4 + 6 + 5 + 7 + 1 =$ __28__

$16 + 4 + 5 + 5 + 7 + 3 =$ __40__

```
                            7
  9 7                       9
  2 3      8, 3 2 7         6
  6 2      6, 0 8 2         8
  5 9      5, 9 1 4         4
+ 4 2    + 6, 8 7 5       + 6
-----    ---------       ---
2 8 3    2 7, 1 9 8       4 0
```

Lesson 5 — 3 min.

```
  4 7 8      6, 3 2 9      $ 1 . 1 4
  2 9 6      8, 4 0 6        8 . 7 2
  5 1 4      9, 3 8 7        6 . 5 3
+ 8 7 2    +   6 5 2      + 9 . 9 1
-------    ---------      ---------
2, 1 6 0    2 4, 7 7 4     $ 2 6 . 3 0


  1 3        1 6        1 4        2 1
-  9       -  8       -  3       -  9
----       ----       ----       ----
   4          8        1 1        1 2


  8 7        4 6        9 1        6 3 1
- 2 9      - 3 7      - 1 4      - 2 0 9
-----      -----      -----      -------
  5 8          9        7 7        4 2 2
```

Lesson	Score
2	
3	
4	
5	

Lesson 6   3 min.

```
  321        $32.56        63
  508         93.72        29
  657        +44.08        48
+ 189       _____       53
_____     $170.36      +19
  1,675                  ____
                           212
```

```
   32         67         29         56
   ×5         ×2         ×3         ×4
  ___        ___        ___        ___
  160        134         87        224
```

```
  371        637        802
 −192       −441       −114
 ____       ____       ____
  179        196        688
```

Lesson 8   1 min. 30 sec.

```
  8         5         9         9         3
 +7        +6        +3        +8        +7
 __        __        __        __        __
 15        11        12        17        10
```

```
 16        12        13        21        17
 −8        −7        −9        −9        −8
 __        __        __        __        __
  8         5         4        12         9
```

```
  6         4         8         9         3
 ×5        ×4        ×4        ×5        ×6
 __        __        __        __        __
 30        16        32        45        18
```

Lesson 9   5 min.

```
 4,682      9,327      1,406
 ×    5     ×    6     ×    3
 _____    _____    _____
 23,410     55,962     4,218
```

```
  431       $4.14      4,872
 +515      +82.93     +5,168
 ____      _____     _____
  946      $87.07     10,040
```

```
  871        395       4,301
 −462       −287      −2,681
 ____       ____      _____
  409        108       1,620
```

Lesson 10   3 min.

```
 8,762      4,962      1,489
 ×    5     ×    7     ×    4
 _____    _____    _____
 43,810     34,734     5,956
```

```
 9,536      2,709      3,995
 ×    7     ×    5     ×    7
 _____    _____    _____
 66,752     13,545     27,965
```

4 dimes + 2 nickels − 1 quarter = __$.25__

Quiz 10 each

Lesson	Score
6	
8	
9	
10	

Quiz 1

Name ——————————————————— Date ———————————————

1. Follow the signs. 5 each (50)

a.
```
  11
   7
+  9
----
  27
```

b.
```
$19.85
 23.06
+48.37
-------
$91.28
```

c.
```
 13
- 7
---
  6
```

d.
```
 200
-188
----
  12
```

e.
```
  5
× 3
---
 15
```

f.
```
316
×  3
----
948
```

g.
```
793
568
+466
-----
1,827
```

h.
```
$73.94
-23.59
-------
$50.35
```

i.
```
 32
× 4
----
128
```

j.
```
379
-216
----
163
```

2. Place commas correctly in these numbers. 2 each (8)

a. 4,3 2 0,6 8 7   **b.** 6 2 9,5 1 8   **c.** 9 5,4 2 7

3. Write these numbers correctly. 5 each (15)

a. ___67,342,615___ 67 million, 342 thousand, 615

b. ___902,892,582___ 902 million, 892 thousand, 582

c. ___86,472,016___ 86 million, 472 thousand, 16

4. Write the values. 5 each (15)

a. 3 dimes = ___$.30 or 30¢___   **b.** 5 nickels = ___$.25 or 25¢___

c. 7 dollars = ___$7.00 or $7___

5. Underline the clue words and write the process sign (+ or −) that would be used to answer the problem. 2 each (12)

a. _____ + _____ How many cookies did they eat <u>in all</u>?

b. _____ − _____ How much <u>less</u> did the box weigh?

c. _____ + _____ How many books did he buy <u>altogether</u>?

$$\begin{array}{r} 9{,}743 \\ \times\ \ \ \ 6 \\ \hline 58{,}458 \end{array} \quad \begin{array}{r} 4{,}182 \\ \times\ \ \ \ 7 \\ \hline 29{,}274 \end{array} \quad \begin{array}{r} 2{,}985 \\ \times\ \ \ \ 4 \\ \hline 11{,}940 \end{array}$$

$$\begin{array}{r} 47 \\ \times\ 26 \\ \hline 1{,}222 \end{array} \quad \begin{array}{r} 35 \\ \times\ 62 \\ \hline 2{,}170 \end{array} \quad \begin{array}{r} 49 \\ \times\ 77 \\ \hline 3{,}773 \end{array}$$

$$\begin{array}{r} 7{,}326 \\ -\ 1{,}478 \\ \hline 5{,}848 \end{array} \quad \begin{array}{r} 2{,}093 \\ -\ 848 \\ \hline 1{,}245 \end{array} \quad \begin{array}{r} \$16{,}001.15 \\ -\ \ \ \ 198.72 \\ \hline \$15{,}802.43 \end{array}$$

$$\begin{array}{r} 87 \\ \times\ 56 \\ \hline 4{,}872 \end{array} \quad \begin{array}{r} 25 \\ \times\ 74 \\ \hline 1{,}850 \end{array} \quad \begin{array}{r} 632 \\ \times\ 21 \\ \hline 13{,}272 \end{array}$$

$6 \times 8 = \underline{\ 48\ }$ $8 + 8 = \underline{\ 16\ }$

$4 \times 3 = \underline{\ 12\ }$ $13 - 6 = \underline{\ 7\ }$

$8 - 3 = \underline{\ 5\ }$ $9 \times 7 = \underline{\ 63\ }$

$19 + 4 = \underline{\ 23\ }$ $5 \times 5 = \underline{\ 25\ }$

$8 \times 7 = \underline{\ 56\ }$ $12 + 8 = \underline{\ 20\ }$

$14 - 6 = \underline{\ 8\ }$ $13 + 9 = \underline{\ 22\ }$

$31 + 7 = \underline{\ 38\ }$ $27 - 6 = \underline{\ 21\ }$

$4 \times 4 = \underline{\ 16\ }$ $4 \times 8 = \underline{\ 32\ }$

$$\begin{array}{r} 9{,}745 \\ \times\ \ \ \ 7 \\ \hline 68{,}215 \end{array} \quad \begin{array}{r} \$48.02 \\ \times\ \ \ \ 6 \\ \hline \$288.12 \end{array} \quad \begin{array}{r} 7{,}149 \\ \times\ \ \ \ 8 \\ \hline 57{,}192 \end{array}$$

$4\overline{\smash{)}8}\ \ ^{2} \qquad 5\overline{\smash{)}10}\ \ ^{2} \qquad 3\overline{\smash{)}9}\ \ ^{3} \qquad 4\overline{\smash{)}12}\ \ ^{3}$

Quiz 6 each

Lesson	Score
11	
13	
14	
15	

Test 1

Grade ☐

Name _____ Date _____

1. Work these story problems on the test paper. 3 each (6)

a. Jack bought a Bible for $8.45.
How much change did he receive
from $10.00? $1.55

b. How much did Suzanne earn by
selling 150 oranges for 6¢ each?
$9.00

2. Follow the signs. 3 each (36)

a. $42.35
+27.29
$69.64

b. 781
× 5
3,905

c. 7,471
−5,489
1,982

d. 162
× 4
648

e. 26
75
54
+83
238

f. 8,112
−1,079
7,033

g. 703
× 6
4,218

h. 7,136
−3,225
3,911

i. $19.37
+ 6.25
$25.62

j. 72
×46
432
+288
3,312

k. 385
293
646
+721
2,045

l. 786
× 5
3,930

3. Write the answers. 3 each (36)

a. $2 + 9 =$ __11__   b. $17 - 9 =$ __8__   c. $7 \times 7 =$ __49__

d. $5 \times 3 =$ __15__   e. $2 \times 8 =$ __16__   f. $5 + 8 =$ __13__

g. $12 - 5 =$ __7__   h. $9 + 9 =$ __18__   i. $11 - 0 =$ __11__

j. $6 \times 7 =$ __42__   k. $8 \times 3 =$ __24__   l. $4 \times 5 =$ __20__

4. Write these numbers correctly. 2 each (6)

a. 23 million, 218 thousand, 6 __23,218,006__

b. 8 million, 9 __8,000,009__

c. 15 million, 350 thousand __15,350,000__

5. Place the dollar sign and decimal point correctly in each to make dollars and cents. 1 each (10)

a. $ 4. 9 5   b. $ 3 2. 9 5   c. $. 6 5   d. $ 9. 7 3

e. $. 2 3   f. $ 7. 0 9   g. $ 6 2. 0 4   h. $ 1. 2 7

i. $ 6. 1 4   j. $ 1 4. 7 5

6. Write the progress sign (+ or −) that would be used to answer the problem. 2 each (6)

a. ____+____ How many students are there altogether?

b. ____−____ How much less did the basketball cost?

c. ____+____ What is the sum of the houses?

Lesson 16 — 5 min.

+	12	9	7	11	8	5
9	21	18	16	20	17	14
3	15	12	10	14	11	8
5	17	14	12	16	13	10
10	22	19	17	21	18	15
8	20	17	15	19	16	13

Quiz 2 each

Lesson 18 — 4 min.

$$\begin{array}{r} 978 \\ \times 28 \\ \hline 27,384 \end{array} \qquad \begin{array}{r} 495 \\ \times 67 \\ \hline 33,165 \end{array} \qquad \begin{array}{r} 382 \\ \times 26 \\ \hline 9,932 \end{array}$$

$$6\overline{\smash{)}306} = 51 \qquad 5\overline{\smash{)}490} = 98 \qquad 7\overline{\smash{)}560} = 80$$

Lesson 19 — 3 min.

$$\begin{array}{r} 97 \\ 29 \\ 56 \\ +82 \\ \hline 264 \end{array} \qquad \begin{array}{r} 632 \\ 549 \\ 876 \\ +615 \\ \hline 2,672 \end{array} \qquad \begin{array}{r} 907 \\ -468 \\ \hline 439 \end{array}$$

$$\begin{array}{r} 9,328 \\ \times\ \ 3 \\ \hline 27,984 \end{array} \qquad \begin{array}{r} \$67.29 \\ \times\ \ \ 8 \\ \hline \$538.32 \end{array} \qquad \begin{array}{r} 43 \\ \times 26 \\ \hline 1,118 \end{array}$$

Lesson 20 — 2 min. 30 sec.

×	11	7	12	3	9	6
9	99	63	108	27	81	54
7	77	49	84	21	63	42
3	33	21	36	9	27	18
8	88	56	96	24	72	48
4	44	28	48	12	36	24

Lesson	Score
16	
18	
19	
20	

Quiz 2

Name _____   Date _____

1. Follow the signs. 5 each (50)

a. $62.83
      − 14.79
      $48.04

b.   7
        × 7
         49

c.   23
          17
        + 84
         124

d. $57.59
        21.13
      + 8.68
       $87.40

e.   13
        − 7
           6

f.   359
        ×   5
        1,795

g.   13
         × 26
           78
         + 26
          338

h.   34
         + 17
           51

i. $10.50
       − 2.77
        $7.73

j.   982
        ×   4
        3,928

2. Divide and check. 2 each part (4)

```
      × 5            5
  5 ⟌ 2 5          × 5
    − 2 5↓         2 5
        0
```

3. Write the products. 2 each (40)

×	8	2	6	4	7
4	32	8	24	16	28
3	24	6	18	12	21
5	40	10	30	20	35
6	48	12	36	24	42

4. Place the commas correctly. 1 each (6)

a. 7,326,458   **b.** 1,900,053,726   **c.** 171,819

Lesson 21 — 3 min.

4 ft. = __48__ in.   6 yd. = __18__ ft.

3 yd. = __108__ in.   36 yd. = __108__ ft.

$$5\overline{)472}\quad 94\,r.2$$

$$6\overline{)219}\quad 36\,r.3$$

$$3\overline{)872}\quad 290\,r.2$$

Lesson 23 — 3 min.

72 ft. = __24__ yd.   13 ft. = __156__ in.

$$\begin{array}{r} 9,728 \\ 4,751 \\ 6,139 \\ +\,8,358 \\ \hline 28,976 \end{array}$$

$$\begin{array}{r} 32,201 \\ -\,17,294 \\ \hline 14,907 \end{array}$$

$$\begin{array}{r} 6,759 \\ \times\quad 8 \\ \hline 54,072 \end{array}$$

Lesson 24 — 2 min.

17 − 8 = __9__   8 × 4 = __32__

23 − 5 = __18__   7 × 6 = __42__

12 − 3 = __9__   3 × 9 = __27__

18 − 9 = __9__   4 × 5 = __20__

14 − 5 = __9__   12 × 2 = __24__

21 − 7 = __14__   5 × 9 = __45__

9 − 6 = __3__   6 × 9 = __54__

33 − 18 = __15__   7 × 8 = __56__

Lesson 25 — 5 min.

×	8	6	4	7	12	3
11	88	66	44	77	132	33
9	72	54	36	63	108	27
12	96	72	48	84	144	36
3	24	18	12	21	36	9
10	80	60	40	70	120	30

Quiz 3 each

Name _____

Lesson	Score
21	
23	
24	
25	

Arithmetic 4

Test 2

Name _____ Date _____

1. Solve these story problems. Do your work on this test sheet. 3 each step (9)

a. On Friday, Joe sold 125 pencils at 15¢ each. How much did he receive for them? $18.75

b. Rebecca bought a stuffed dog for $4.97 and a game for $9.98. How much change did she receive from $20.00? (1) $14.95; (2) $5.05

2. Follow the signs. 3 each (30)

a.
```
   6,000
 − 3,684
─────────
   2,316
```

b.
```
   3,631
   7,507
 + 1,078
─────────
  12,216
```

c.
```
    947
 ×    5
────────
  4,735
```

d.
```
   3,180
 − 2,058
─────────
   1,122
```

e.
```
    925
    298
    523
 +  233
────────
  1,979
```

f.
```
    407
 ×   39
────────
  15,873
```

g.
```
  $50.00
 − 45.25
─────────
  $4.75
```

h.
```
   5,381
 + 2,199
─────────
   7,580
```

i.
```
    268
 ×   46
────────
  12,328
```

j.
```
     76
     70
     34
     17
 +   23
────────
    220
```

3. Match. Put the correct letter in each blank. 2 each (18)

_____u_____ **a.** Change measures from larger to smaller by ___.   **r.** difference

_____s_____ **b.** Change measures from smaller to larger by ___.   **s.** dividing

_____w_____ **c.** Three feet equal ___.   **t.** in all

_____t_____ **d.** Addition clue words   **u.** multiplying

_____y_____ **e.** Answer to a division problem   **v.** one foot

_____r_____ **f.** Answer to a subtraction problem   **w.** one yard

_____v_____ **g.** Twelve inches equal ___.   **x.** product

_____x_____ **h.** Answer to a multiplication problem   **y.** quotient

_____z_____ **i.** One yard equals ___.   **z.** thirty-six inches

4. Divide and check. 2 each step (12)

a. 4)376   94 × 4 376   **b.** 8)728   91 × 8 728   **c.** 7)504   72 × 7 504

5. Write the products. 1 each (26)

×	12	6	11	1	10	2	9	3	8	4	7	5	0
6	72	36	66	6	60	12	54	18	48	24	42	30	0
4	48	24	44	4	40	8	36	12	32	16	28	20	0

6. Work carefully. 1 each (3)

a. 3 yd. = ___9___ ft.   **b.** 24 ft. = ___8___ yd.   **c.** 3 ft. = ___36___ in.

Lesson 26 — 3 min.

$$6\overline{)504} \quad 84$$
$$3\overline{)873} \quad 291$$
$$7\overline{)609} \quad 87$$

$$\begin{array}{r} 954 \\ \times\ 36 \\ \hline 34{,}344 \end{array} \qquad \begin{array}{r} 278 \\ \times\ 59 \\ \hline 16{,}402 \end{array} \qquad \begin{array}{r} 482 \\ \times\ 64 \\ \hline 30{,}848 \end{array}$$

Lesson 28 — 5 min.

$$\begin{array}{r} 4 \\ \times\ 8 \\ \hline 32 \end{array} \quad \begin{array}{r} 3 \\ \times\ 7 \\ \hline 21 \end{array} \quad \begin{array}{r} 2 \\ \times\ 9 \\ \hline 18 \end{array} \quad \begin{array}{r} 6 \\ \times\ 6 \\ \hline 36 \end{array} \quad \begin{array}{r} 8 \\ \times\ 9 \\ \hline 72 \end{array}$$

$$\begin{array}{r} 9 \\ +\ 7 \\ \hline 16 \end{array} \quad \begin{array}{r} 6 \\ +\ 8 \\ \hline 14 \end{array} \quad \begin{array}{r} 14 \\ +\ 3 \\ \hline 17 \end{array} \quad \begin{array}{r} 7 \\ +\ 7 \\ \hline 14 \end{array} \quad \begin{array}{r} 8 \\ +\ 9 \\ \hline 17 \end{array}$$

$$\begin{array}{r} 13 \\ -\ 6 \\ \hline 7 \end{array} \quad \begin{array}{r} 19 \\ -\ 11 \\ \hline 8 \end{array} \quad \begin{array}{r} 17 \\ -\ 8 \\ \hline 9 \end{array} \quad \begin{array}{r} 14 \\ -\ 7 \\ \hline 7 \end{array} \quad \begin{array}{r} 21 \\ -\ 6 \\ \hline 15 \end{array}$$

$$72 \div 6 = \underline{12} \qquad 24 \div 8 = \underline{3}$$

Quiz 5 each

Lesson 29 — 2 min.

+	12	7	9	3	8	6
4	16	11	13	7	12	10
13	25	20	22	16	21	19
9	21	16	18	12	17	15
7	19	14	16	10	15	13
11	23	18	20	14	19	17

Lesson 30 — 3 min.

$$\begin{array}{r} 683 \\ \times\ 86 \\ \hline 58{,}738 \end{array} \qquad \begin{array}{r} 459 \\ \times\ 27 \\ \hline 12{,}393 \end{array} \qquad \begin{array}{r} 796 \\ \times\ 89 \\ \hline 70{,}844 \end{array}$$

$$\begin{array}{r} \$351.06 \\ -\ 29.73 \\ \hline \$321.33 \end{array} \qquad \begin{array}{r} 6{,}251 \\ -4{,}836 \\ \hline 1{,}415 \end{array} \qquad \begin{array}{r} 2{,}391 \\ -\ 888 \\ \hline 1{,}503 \end{array}$$

Lesson	Score
26	
28	
29	
30	

Quiz 3

Name _____ Date _____

1. Write the products. 2 each (36)

×	3	10	6	12	7	2
7	21	70	42	84	49	14
9	27	90	54	108	63	18
4	12	40	24	48	28	8

2. Follow the signs. 5 each (45)

a.
```
  7 9 1
  2 8 5
+ 3 6 6
───────
1, 4 4 2
```

b.
```
  8 0
- 1 9
─────
  6 1
```

c.
```
  2 9 1
×     6
───────
1, 7 4 6
```

d.
```
  3 8
  4 2
+ 7 6
─────
1 5 6
```

e.
```
  2 4
× 1 5
─────
1 2 0
+ 2 4
─────
3 6 0
```

f.
```
  2, 9 9 7
+ 3, 5 8 6
─────────
  6, 5 8 3
```

g.
```
    3
× 5 0
─────
1 5 0
```

h.
```
       × 9 r. 2
  5 | 4 7 |
  - 4 5 ↓
  ───────
       2
```

i.
```
     × 9
 4 | 3 6 |
 - 3 6 ↓
 ───────
      0
```

3. Write the answers. 5 each (15)

a. 1 yd. = __3__ ft.   **b.** 1 ft. = __12__ in.   **c.** 1 mi. = _5,280_ ft.

Lesson 31 — 3 min.

Average.

9 7	4 3 7	4 1
8 6	6 9 2	5 6
9 3	4 1 6	4 8
8 8	8 9 1	3 9
9 1		2 4
8 5	4/2,436/609	4 4
6/540/90		6/252/42

Lesson 33 — 2 min.

$72 \div 6 =$ _12_ $8 \times 7 =$ _56_

$48 \div 8 =$ _6_ $4 \times 3 =$ _12_

$36 \div 9 =$ _4_ $5 \times 6 =$ _30_

$70 \div 10 =$ _7_ $12 \times 11 =$ _132_

$35 \div 7 =$ _5_ $7 \times 9 =$ _63_

$16 \div 4 =$ _4_ $8 \times 4 =$ _32_

$28 \div 7 =$ _4_ $2 \times 11 =$ _22_

$56 \div 8 =$ _7_ $4 \times 6 =$ _24_

Lesson 34 — 5 min.

$$\begin{array}{r} 1\ 9 \\ 4\overline{)7\ 6} \end{array} \qquad \begin{array}{r} 1\ 1\ \text{r.}\ 4 \\ 8\overline{)9\ 2} \end{array} \qquad \begin{array}{r} 4\ 5\ \text{r.}\ 6 \\ 7\overline{)3\ 2\ 1} \end{array}$$

6, 3 2 1	4, 0 9 2	1, 4 7 9
× 7	× 6	× 8
4 4, 2 4 7	2 4, 5 5 2	1 1, 8 3 2

9 3 2	4 2 1	5 1 6
+ 6 8 7	+ 4 3 7	+ 9 7 8
1, 6 1 9	8 5 8	1, 4 9 4

Lesson 35 — 2 min.

×	11	7	12	3	6	9
9	99	63	108	27	54	81
7	77	49	84	21	42	63
10	110	70	120	30	60	90
6	66	42	72	18	36	54
4	44	28	48	12	24	36

Quiz 8 each

Lesson	Score
31	
33	
34	
35	

Test 3

Name _____ Date _____

1. Solve these story problems. Do your work on this test sheet. 3 each (6)

   a. Jim paid $6.00 to ride a bicycle for 4 hours. At that rate, what was the cost per hour? $1.50

   b. Sue collected 12 shells Monday, 15 shells Tuesday, and 21 shells Wednesday. How many shells did she collect those three days?
   48 shells

2. Circle the digit in the one thousands' position. 3 each (9)

   a. 5 3, 2 0 6   **b.** 3 2 9, 5 8 6   **c.** 4, 8 0 3

3. Fill in the blanks. 3 each (18)

   a. 1 yd. = ___3___ ft.   **b.** 1 ton = _2,000_ lb.   **c.** 1 lb. = ___16___ oz.

   d. 1 ft. = ___12___ in.   **e.** 1 mi. = _5,280_ ft.   **f.** 1 yd. = ___36___ in.

4. Divide and check. 2 each part (12)

   a.
$$7\overline{)525} = 75 \qquad \begin{array}{r} 75 \\ \times\ 7 \\ \hline 525 \end{array}$$

   b.
$$3\overline{)7,198} = 2{,}399\ r.\ 1 \qquad \begin{array}{r} 2{,}399 \\ \times\quad 3 \\ \hline 7197 \\ +\quad 1 \\ \hline 7{,}198 \end{array}$$

   c.
$$5\overline{)6,670} = 1{,}334 \qquad \begin{array}{r} 1{,}334 \\ \times\quad 5 \\ \hline 6{,}670 \end{array}$$

Occupation was one of the pleasures of paradise, and we cannot be happy without it. —Anna Jameson

5. Average by dividing the sum by the number of addends. 2 each step (8)

a. 16, 28, 16, 20 = 80
　　　　　20

b. $.98, $1.27, $.93 = $3.18
　　　　　$1.06

6. Follow the signs. 3 each (15)

a.
```
  9 0
  1 5
  2 9
  9 4
+ 3 3
-----
  2 6 1
```

b.
```
  4, 8 5 6
- 4, 5 7 1
---------
    2 8 5
```

c.
```
  3, 9 5 8
×       7
---------
 2 7, 7 0 6
```

d.
```
    2 7 5
×    4 3
-------
 1 1, 8 2 5
```

e.
```
  3 4 1
  5 8 9
  2 5 6
+ 6 6 3
-------
  1, 8 4 9
```

7. Fill in the blanks. 2 each (24)

a. 7 × 9 = __63__

b. 15 + 8 = __23__

c. 28 ÷ 4 = __7__

d. 81 ÷ 9 = __9__

e. 6 × 9 = __54__

f. 19 − 8 = __11__

g. 8 + 6 = __14__

h. 56 ÷ 7 = __8__

i. 13 + 9 = __22__

j. 12 − 5 = __7__

k. 21 − 6 = __15__

l. 9 × 8 = __72__

8. Solve the measurement equations. 3 each (6)

a. 8 oz. + 3 lb. = __56__ oz.

b. 24 yd. − 9 ft. = __21__ yd.

Lesson 36   2 min.

Write +, −, ×, or ÷.

6 $\underline{\times}$ 3 = 18   16 $\underline{+}$ 6 = 22

4 $\underline{\times}$ 2 = 8   13 $\underline{-}$ 9 = 4

12 $\underline{\div}$ 2 = 6   22 $\underline{-}$ 11 = 11

27 $\underline{+}$ 4 = 31   35 $\underline{\div}$ 5 = 7

18 $\underline{-}$ 9 = 9   4 $\underline{\times}$ 8 = 32

18 $\underline{\div}$ 3 = 6   9 $\underline{-}$ 7 = 2

9 $\underline{\times}$ 3 = 27   54 $\underline{\div}$ 6 = 9

Lesson 38   2 min.

×	9	10	7	12	5	11
8	72	80	56	96	40	88
12	108	120	84	144	60	132
9	81	90	63	108	45	99
6	54	60	42	72	30	66
10	90	100	70	120	50	110

Lesson 39   5 min.

$\frac{1}{3}$ of 15 = $\underline{5}$ $\frac{1}{7}$ of 49 = $\underline{7}$

$\frac{1}{9}$ of 81 = $\underline{9}$ $\frac{1}{11}$ of 33 = $\underline{3}$

$\frac{1}{11}$ of 121 = $\underline{11}$ $\frac{1}{5}$ of 35 = $\underline{7}$

$\frac{1}{10}$ of 100 = $\underline{10}$ $\frac{1}{7}$ of 49 = $\underline{7}$

$\frac{1}{5}$ of 10 = $\underline{2}$ $\frac{1}{9}$ of 18 = $\underline{2}$

$\frac{1}{12}$ of 60 = $\underline{5}$ $\frac{1}{6}$ of 36 = $\underline{6}$

$\frac{1}{7}$ of 14 = $\underline{2}$ $\frac{1}{5}$ of 25 = $\underline{5}$

$\frac{1}{12}$ of 72 = $\underline{6}$ $\frac{1}{2}$ of 16 = $\underline{8}$

$\frac{1}{10}$ of 50 = $\underline{5}$ $\frac{1}{9}$ of 72 = $\underline{8}$

$\frac{1}{3}$ of 27 = $\underline{9}$ $\frac{1}{8}$ of 48 = $\underline{6}$

Lesson 40   3 min. 30 sec.

$$\begin{array}{r} 492 \\ \times\ 123 \\ \hline 60,516 \end{array} \qquad \begin{array}{r} 609 \\ \times\ 415 \\ \hline 252,735 \end{array} \qquad \begin{array}{r} 587 \\ \times\ 426 \\ \hline 250,062 \end{array}$$

$$4\overline{)16}\ ^{4} \qquad 7\overline{)35}\ ^{5} \qquad 3\overline{)27}\ ^{9}$$

Quiz 4 each

27

Lesson	Score
36	
38	
39	
40	

Quiz 4

Name _____ Date _____

1. Match. Write the correct letter in each blank. 4 each (24)

a. __y__ To change a larger measure to a smaller measure, ___.

b. __w__ To average numbers, ___.

c. __u__ The five steps in division are ___.

d. __z__ The denominator of a fraction ___.

e. __v__ To change a smaller measure to a larger measure, ___.

f. __x__ To check division, ___.

u. $\div \times - c$ ↓

v. divide

w. divide the sum by the number of addends

x. multiply the quotient by the divisor and add the remainder

y. multiply

z. tells how many parts the object is divided into

2. Fill in the blanks with the correct number. 3 each (18)

a. $6 \times \underline{\ 9\ } = 54$

b. $\underline{\ 49\ } \div 7 = 7$

c. $37 - 19 = \underline{\ 18\ }$

d. $12 \div \underline{\ 3\ } = 4$

e. $19 + \underline{\ 23\ } = 42$

f. $\underline{\ 8\ } \times 12 = 96$

3. Fill in the blanks. 3 each (18)

a. 1 yd. = __3__ ft.

b. 1 lb. = __16__ oz.

c. 1 t. = __2,000__ lb.

d. 1 ft. = __12__ in.

e. 1 yd. = __36__ in.

f. 1 gal. = __4__ qt.

4. Follow the signs. 5 each (40)

a.
```
  2 7
  1 8
  4 6
+ 7 5
-----
1 6 6
```

b.
```
  2, 7 0 6
- 1, 1 1 7
---------
  1, 5 8 9
```

c.
```
  6 7 9
×     4
-------
2, 7 1 6
```

d.
```
  7, 8 5 1
+ 2, 9 9 9
----------
1 0, 8 5 0
```

e.
```
  5, 0 0 0
- 2, 2 9 7
----------
  2, 7 0 3
```

f.
```
    3 6 5
×    2 3
--------
  1 0 9 5
+ 7 3 0
--------
  8, 3 9 5
```

g.
```
    × 7 8
  4 ⟌ 3 1 2
  - 2 8 ↓
  -------
      3 2
    - 3 2
    -----
        0
```

h. $9 \times 7 = \underline{\ 6 3\ }$

Average.

```
9 1 3        1 5        9 3 2
6 8 2        1 9        6 2 1
4 5 1        8 3        4 8 7
             6 5
3/2,046/682  4 3        3/2,040/680

             5/225/45
```

+	17	9	11	13	4	0
8	25	17	19	21	12	8
6	23	15	17	19	10	6
9	26	18	20	22	13	9
4	21	13	15	17	8	4
5	22	14	16	18	9	5

```
      3          3          2
20│6 0      30│9 0      41│8 2
```

```
  9 3 2        4 9 9        3 7 6
×     6        ×   8        ×   5
5 , 5 9 2      3 , 9 9 2    1 , 8 8 0
```

```
    9 7        4 3 2        6 1 7
−   6 9      − 2 0 9      − 1 8 8
    2 8        2 2 3        4 2 9
```

```
    9        6        4        3      1 2
×   7      × 5      × 8      × 9      × 8
  6 3      3 0      3 2      2 7      9 6
```

```
  1 8      2 7      1 4        9        7
+   9      + 6      + 3      + 8      + 8
  2 7      3 3      1 7      1 7      1 5
```

```
  7 3      1 9      2 1      1 3      4 2
−   6      − 7      − 8      − 9    − 1 1
  6 7      1 2      1 3        4      3 1
```

Quiz 8 each

Lesson	Score
41	
43	
44	
45	

Test 4

Name _____ Date _____

1. Solve these story problems. Do your work on the test sheet. 3 each (6)

a. Jeffrey's father paid $38 for him to spend 2 days at a Christian camp. What was the cost per day?
$19

b. Sierra bought 31 balloons at 15¢ each for her class party. How much did Sierra pay? $4.65

2. Solve these measurement problems. Show your work. 2 each (6)

a. 3 ft. = __36__ in.

b. 15 ft. = __5__ yd.

c. 3 lb. + 2 oz. = __50__ oz.

3. Average. 2 each step (12)

a.		**b.**		**c.**	
18		$1.30		50	
23		$1.42		76	
14	20	$ .97	$1.23	54	65
25				80	
20					

4. Give the fraction for the shaded portion. 4 each (12)

a.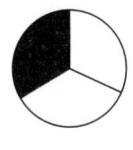

$\frac{1}{3}$

b.

$\frac{5}{8}$

c.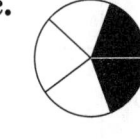

$\frac{2}{5}$

*Resolved, never to do anything which I should be afraid to do
if it were the last hour of my life.* —Jonathan Edwards

5. Find the fractional parts of these whole numbers. 3 each (12)

a. $\frac{1}{3}$ of 27 = __9__   **b.** $\frac{1}{7}$ of 35 = __5__   **c.** $\frac{1}{6}$ of 42 = __7__   **d.** $\frac{1}{2}$ of 10 = __5__

6. Divide and check. 2 each step (12)

a.
$$\begin{array}{r} 243 \\ 3\overline{)729} \end{array} \quad \begin{array}{r} 243 \\ \times\ \ 3 \\ \hline 729 \end{array}$$

b.
$$\begin{array}{r} 153\,r.3 \\ 4\overline{)615} \end{array} \quad \begin{array}{r} 153 \\ \times\ \ 4 \\ \hline 612 \\ +\ \ \ 3 \\ \hline 615 \end{array}$$

c.
$$\begin{array}{r} 1{,}291 \\ 6\overline{)7{,}746} \end{array} \quad \begin{array}{r} 1{,}291 \\ \times\ \ \ \ \ 6 \\ \hline 7{,}746 \end{array}$$

7. Follow the signs. Work carefully. 3 each (15)

a.
$$\begin{array}{r} 340 \\ 764 \\ +509 \\ \hline 1{,}613 \end{array}$$

b.
$$\begin{array}{r} 8{,}017 \\ -3{,}088 \\ \hline 4{,}929 \end{array}$$

c.
$$\begin{array}{r} 3{,}801 \\ \times\ \ \ \ \ 7 \\ \hline 26{,}607 \end{array}$$

d.
$$\begin{array}{r} 679 \\ \times 24 \\ \hline 16{,}296 \end{array}$$

e.
$$\begin{array}{r} 742 \\ \times 123 \\ \hline 91{,}266 \end{array}$$

8. Write the products. 1 each (21)

×	7	9	5	3	8	4	6
7	49	63	35	21	56	28	42
5	35	45	25	15	40	20	30
6	42	54	30	18	48	24	36

Circle digit in the hundreds' position.

4,③2 9   16,③0 7   ②8 7   14,⑨3 1
⑧0 6   49,⑧9 2   ④1 6   5,③7 2

Circle digit in the tens' position.

4,3②9   16,3⓪7   28⑧7   14,93①1... 14,9③1
80⓪6   49,8⑨2   4①6   5,3⑦2

Circle digit in the ones' position.

4,32⑨   16,30⑦   28⑦   14,93①
80⑥   49,89②   41⑥   5,37②

×	8	10	11	12	7	9
12	96	120	132	144	84	108
9	72	90	99	108	63	81
7	56	70	77	84	49	63
10	80	100	110	120	70	90
8	64	80	88	96	56	72

Quiz 3 each

$$42\overline{)84}\quad\ ^2$$ $$41\overline{)41}\quad\ ^1$$ $$21\overline{)840}\quad\ ^{40}$$

$$\begin{array}{r}673\\ \times239\\ \hline 160,847\end{array}\qquad \begin{array}{r}163\\ \times37\\ \hline 6,031\end{array}\qquad \begin{array}{r}595\\ \times268\\ \hline 159,460\end{array}$$

Average.

96   257   1,832
87   465   4,781
33   6,593
24   2/722/361
                         3/13,206/4,402
4/240/60

Lesson	Score
46	
48	
49	
50	

Quiz 5

Name _____ Date _____

1. Write the products. 3 each (36)

a. $3 \times 5 =$ _15_   **b.** $4 \times 4 =$ _16_   **c.** $6 \times 7 =$ _42_

d. $4 \times 7 =$ _28_   **e.** $7 \times 5 =$ _35_   **f.** $9 \times 6 =$ _54_

g. $12 \times 8 =$ _96_   **h.** $3 \times 9 =$ _27_   **i.** $10 \times 5 =$ _50_

j. $14 \times 3 =$ _42_   **k.** $20 \times 7 =$ _140_   **l.** $32 \times 4 =$ _128_

2. Divide and write the remainder as a fraction. 5 each (20)

a. $4\overline{)13}$ $3\frac{1}{4}$ **b.** $7\overline{)27}$ $3\frac{6}{7}$ **c.** $6\overline{)13}$ $2\frac{1}{6}$ **d.** $5\overline{)28}$ $5\frac{3}{5}$

3. Write the answers. 5 each (15)

a. 1 yd. = _3_ ft.   **b.** 1 lb. = _16_ oz.   **c.** 1 gal. = _4_ qt.

4. Find the answers. 5 each (25)

a.
$$\frac{3}{11}$$
$$\frac{2}{11}$$
$$+\frac{4}{11}$$
$$\overline{\frac{9}{11}}$$

b.
$$\begin{array}{r} 73 \\ 59 \\ 76 \\ +84 \\ \hline 292 \end{array}$$

c.
$$\begin{array}{r} 3{,}021 \\ -2{,}783 \\ \hline 238 \end{array}$$

d.
$$\begin{array}{r} 25 \\ \times 14 \\ \hline 100 \\ +25 \\ \hline 350 \end{array}$$

e.
$$\begin{array}{r} \$50.00 \\ -17.85 \\ \hline \$32.15 \end{array}$$

Lesson 51　　5 min.

×	9	5	7	12	2	6
7	63	35	49	84	14	42
6	54	30	42	72	12	36
4	36	20	28	48	8	24
8	72	40	56	96	16	48
11	99	55	77	132	22	66

Lesson 53　　3 min.

$$
\begin{array}{r} 197 \\ 632 \\ +421 \\ \hline 1,250 \end{array}
\qquad
\begin{array}{r} 682 \\ -409 \\ \hline 273 \end{array}
\qquad
\begin{array}{r} 279 \\ \times\ 6 \\ \hline 1,674 \end{array}
\qquad
\begin{array}{r} 42 \\ 57 \\ +26 \\ \hline 125 \end{array}
$$

$$
\begin{array}{r} 692 \\ 506 \\ +813 \\ \hline 2,011 \end{array}
\qquad
\begin{array}{r} 908 \\ \times 14 \\ \hline 12,712 \end{array}
\qquad
\begin{array}{r} 921 \\ -876 \\ \hline 45 \end{array}
\qquad
\begin{array}{r} 498 \\ \times\ 8 \\ \hline 3,984 \end{array}
$$

Quiz 3 each

Lesson 54　　2 min.

×	6	3	7	10	12
4	24	12	28	40	48
9	54	27	63	90	108
12	72	36	84	120	144
5	30	15	35	50	60
8	48	24	56	80	96

Lesson 55　　3 min.

Average.

$$
\begin{array}{r} 68 \\ 44 \\ 29 \\ 37 \\ 42 \\ \hline \end{array}
$$
5/220/44

$$
\begin{array}{r} \$3.20 \\ 6.91 \\ 4.02 \\ \hline \end{array}
$$
3/\$14.13/\$4.71

$$
\begin{array}{r} 11 \\ 9 \\ 13 \\ 21 \\ 17 \\ 13 \\ \hline \end{array}
$$
6/84/14

Lesson	Score
51	
53	
54	
55	

Test 5

Grade ☐

Name _____ Date _____

1. Solve these story problems. Do your work on this test sheet. 3 each (6)

    a. Joel weighed $76\frac{1}{5}$ pounds last year.
Now he weighs $79\frac{3}{5}$ pounds. How
many more pounds does he weigh
now? $3\frac{2}{5}$ pounds

    b. The bookstore at Emmanuel Christian
School bought 72 folders for $9.36.
What was the cost per folder?
$ .13

2. Follow the signs. 3 each (15)

762				
928				
514				
a. 363	**b.** 4,621	**c.** 546	**d.** 2,754	**e.** 279
+ 210	− 1,745	× 63	+ 1,998	× 451
2,777	2,876	34,398	4,752	125,829

3. Divide. 2 each (8)

    a. $9\overline{)3,825}$ 425

    b. $23\overline{)1,196}$ 52

    c. $40\overline{)351}$ 8 r. 31

    d. $44\overline{)1,408}$ 32

4. Solve these measurement problems. 3 each (9)

    a. 5 lb. = __80__ oz.   **b.** 6 ft. − 2 yd. = __0__ ft.   **c.** 2 in. + 2 ft. = __26__ in.

5. Find the answer. 3 each (12)

    a. $\frac{6}{11} + \frac{4}{11} = \frac{10}{11}$ **b.** $\frac{9}{15} + \frac{5}{15} - \frac{4}{15} + \frac{1}{15} = \frac{11}{15}$

    c. $\frac{16}{17} - \frac{9}{17} = \frac{7}{17}$ **d.** $\frac{2}{8} - \frac{1}{8} + \frac{4}{8} = \frac{5}{8}$

6. Circle the larger in each pair. 2 each (16)

    a. (inch) centimeter   **b.** $\left(\frac{3}{4}\right)$; $\frac{1}{4}$ **c.** decimeter; (meter)   **d.** $\left(\frac{7}{8}\right)$ $\frac{5}{8}$

    e. ounce; (pound)   **f.** $\frac{9}{10}$; $\left(\frac{10}{10}\right)$ **g.** (decameter) meter   **h.** $\frac{1}{3}$; $\left(\frac{2}{3}\right)$

7. Write the correct answer. 2 each (14)

    a. __3__ feet = 1 yard   **b.** __4__ quarts = 1 gallon

    c. __16__ ounces = 1 pound   **d.** __8__ fluid ounces = 1 cup

    e. __100__ centimeters = 1 meter   **f.** __12__ inches = 1 foot

    g. __1,000__ meters = 1 kilometer

8. Divide. 2 each (20)

÷	63	81	108	27	54	18	36	9	45	72
9	7	9	12	3	6	2	4	1	5	8

4 ft. + 3 yd. = __13__ ft.

21 da. − 2 wk. = __1__ wk.

3 meters + 7 hectometers = __703__ meters

5 tons − 13 pounds = __9,987__ pounds

$48 \div 8 =$ __6__ $16 \div 4 =$ __4__

$72 \div 9 =$ __8__ $70 \div 7 =$ __10__

$21 \div 3 =$ __7__ $63 \div 9 =$ __7__

$$
\begin{array}{ccccc}
12 & 3 & 4 & 11 & 7 \\
\times 6 & \times 9 & \times 8 & \times 9 & \times 6 \\
\hline
72 & 27 & 32 & 99 & 42
\end{array}
$$

$\frac{1}{7}$ of 56 = __8__ $\frac{1}{9}$ of 18 = __2__

Quiz 6 each

Write any two factors for each.

Answers will vary.

32 __1, 2, 4, 8, 16, 32__   16 __1, 2, 4, 8, 16__

64 __1, 2, 4, 8, 16, 32, 64__   56 __1, 2, 4, 7, 8, 14, 28, 56__

54 __1, 2, 3, 6, 9, 18, 27, 54__   20 __1, 2, 4, 5, 10, 20__

70 __1, 2, 5, 7, 10, 14, 35, 70__   15 __1, 3, 5, 15__

24 __1, 2, 3, 4, 6, 8, 12, 24__   96 __1, 2, 3, 4, 6, 8, 12, 16, 24, 32, 48, 96__

$$
\begin{array}{r}
47\frac{2}{9} \\
16\frac{1}{9} \\
+ 83\frac{1}{9} \\
\hline
146\frac{4}{9}
\end{array}
\qquad
\begin{array}{r}
93\frac{1}{5} \\
87\frac{1}{5} \\
+ 98\frac{2}{5} \\
\hline
278\frac{4}{5}
\end{array}
\qquad
\begin{array}{r}
4{,}326\frac{4}{11} \\
9{,}587\frac{2}{11} \\
+ 1{,}032\frac{4}{11} \\
\hline
14{,}945\frac{10}{11}
\end{array}
$$

$$
\begin{array}{r} 3 \\ 9\overline{)27} \end{array}
\qquad
\begin{array}{r} 21 \\ 32\overline{)672} \end{array}
\qquad
\begin{array}{r} \$4.98 \\ 4\overline{)\$19.92} \end{array}
$$

Lesson	Score
56	
58	
59	
60	

Quiz 6

Name _____ Date _____

1. Fill in the blanks. Choose your answers from the box. An answer may be used twice. 5 each (25)

divide	numerator	multiply	denominator

a. When adding and subtracting fractions with a common denominator, the _____denominator_____ stays the same.

b. The top number in a fraction is called the _____numerator_____.

c. The bottom number in a fraction is called the _____denominator_____.

d. To change measures from smaller to larger, _____divide_____.

e. To change measures from larger to smaller, _____multiply_____.

2. Add or subtract. 5 each (15)

$$2\frac{1}{12}$$

a. $6\frac{5}{12}$ b. $25\frac{3}{4}$ c. $12\frac{2}{3}$

$+3\frac{1}{12}$ $-10\frac{2}{4}$ $-10\frac{1}{3}$

$\overline{11\frac{7}{12}}$ $\overline{15\frac{1}{4}}$ $\overline{2\frac{1}{3}}$

3. Find the products. 1 each (33)

×	2	9	7	4	11	0	5	8	3	10	1
7	14	63	49	28	77	0	35	56	21	70	7
9	18	81	63	36	99	0	45	72	27	90	9
6	12	54	42	24	66	0	30	48	18	60	6

4. Circle the larger in each pair. 5 each (20)

a. inch—(foot)   b. (year)—month

c. meter—(hectometer)   d. pint—(gallon)

×	10	6	5	12	4	9
7	70	42	35	84	28	63
3	30	18	15	36	12	27
11	110	66	55	132	44	99
1	10	6	5	12	4	9
5	50	30	25	60	20	45

Label.

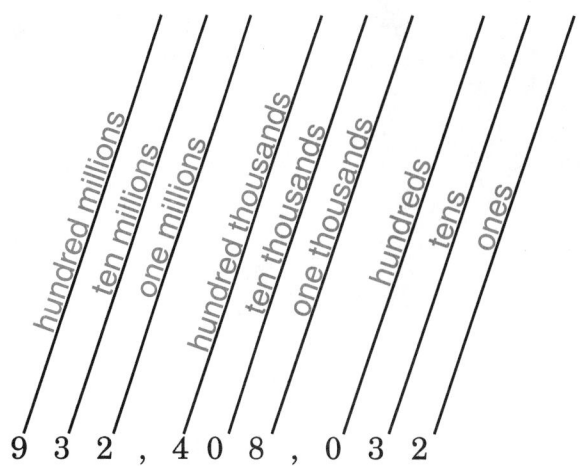

hundred millions · ten millions · one millions · hundred thousands · ten thousands · one thousands · hundreds · tens · ones

9 3 2 , 4 0 8 , 0 3 2

$7\frac{3}{16}$

$18\frac{5}{16}$
$+ 9\frac{7}{16}$
$34\frac{15}{16}$

$21\frac{5}{8}$
$- 13\frac{4}{8}$
$8\frac{1}{8}$

$12\frac{1}{2}$
$- 9$
$3\frac{1}{2}$

$\frac{5}{19}$

$\frac{7}{19}$

$+ \frac{6}{19}$
$\frac{18}{19}$

$\begin{array}{r} 3\,2\,5 \\ \times\,4\,8 \\ \hline 1\,5,6\,0\,0 \end{array}$

$9\overline{)4,306}$ 478 r. 4

$7 \times \underline{\ 4\ } = 28$ $17 - \underline{\ 8\ } = 9$

$16 + \underline{\ 3\ } = 19$ $5 \times \underline{\ 12\ } = 60$

$\underline{\ 48\ } \div 4 = 12$ $23 - 19 = \underline{\ 4\ }$

$17 + 19 = \underline{\ 36\ }$ $64 \div \underline{\ 8\ } = 8$

$\underline{\ 9\ } \times 8 = 72$ $36 + \underline{\ 1\ } = 37$

$5 \times 6 = \underline{\ 30\ }$ $\underline{\ 7\ } \div 7 = 1$

$12 \div \underline{\ 2\ } = 6$ $25 \times \underline{\ 3\ } = 75$

$56 \div 7 = \underline{\ 8\ }$ $16 - 7 = \underline{\ 9\ }$

Quiz 5 each

Lesson	Score
61	
63	
64	
65	

Test 6

Name _____ Date _____

1. Solve these story problems. Do your work on this test sheet. 3 each (6)

a. Joseph and Allison were measured at the doctor's office. Joseph was $62\frac{3}{4}$ inches tall, and Allison was $58\frac{2}{4}$ inches tall. How much taller was Joseph than Allison? $4\frac{1}{4}$ inches

b. Jared's dad drove his car at the average speed of 53 miles per hour for 5 hours. How far did he travel? 265 miles

2. Complete this chart. 2 each (10)

(Each number must have all pairs of factors and factors to be correct.)

Number	Pairs of Factors	Factors
8	(1×8), (2×4)	1, 2, 4, 8
12	(1×12), (2×6), (3×4)	1, 2, 3, 4, 6, 12
4	(1×4), (2×2)	1, 2, 4
15	(1×15), (3×5)	1, 3, 5, 15
18	(1×18), (2×9), (3×6)	1, 2, 3, 6, 9, 18

3. Divide and check. 2 each part (8)

a.
```
        4 3 9 r. 5        4 3 9
    7 ) 3,0 7 8          ×     7
                         3 0 7 3
                       +       5
                         3,0 7 8
```

b.
```
         4 2 r. 4         4 2
   2 1 ) 8 8 6           × 2 1
                           4 2
                        + 8 4
                          8 8 2
                        +     4
                          8 8 6
```

For the Lord giveth wisdom: out of His mouth cometh
knowledge and understanding. —Prov. 2:6

4. Follow the signs. 3 each (30)

$$2\frac{1}{12}$$

a. $8\frac{5}{16}$ **b.** $1\frac{2}{12}$ **c.** $5\frac{5}{6}$ **d.** $7\frac{4}{16}$

$$-\ 3\frac{2}{16}$$ $$+\ 3\frac{2}{12}$$ $$-\ 4\frac{4}{6}$$ $$+\ 2\frac{5}{16}$$

$$5\frac{3}{16}$$ $$6\frac{5}{12}$$ $$1\frac{1}{6}$$ $$9\frac{9}{16}$$

e. $3\frac{2}{5}$ **f.** $\begin{array}{r}5\ 2\ 4\\8\ 6\ 2\\3\ 4\ 8\\+\ 6\ 5\ 7\\\hline 2,3\ 9\ 1\end{array}$ **g.** $\begin{array}{r}4,1\ 5\ 2\\-\ 1,4\ 1\ 3\\\hline 2,7\ 3\ 9\end{array}$ **h.** $\begin{array}{r}9\ 1\ 2\\\times\ 6\ 1\ 8\\\hline 5\ 6\ 3,6\ 1\ 6\end{array}$

$$-\ 2\frac{1}{5}$$

$$1\frac{1}{5}$$

i. $\begin{array}{r}\$2\ 4.3\ 9\\\times\ \ \ \ \ 8\ 5\\\hline \$2,0\ 7\ 3.1\ 5\end{array}$ **j.** $\begin{array}{r}2,4\ 5\ 0\\\times\ \ \ \ \ \ \ 7\\\hline 1\ 7,1\ 5\ 0\end{array}$

5. Fill in the blanks. 3 each (30)

a. 1 gallon = __4__ quarts   **b.** 1 year = __12__ months

c. 1 ton = _2,000_ pounds   **d.** 1 pound = __16__ ounces

e. 1 hectometer = __100__ meters   **f.** 1 yard = __36__ inches

g. 1 week = __7__ days   **h.** 1 century = __100__ years

i. 1 foot = __12__ inches   **j.** 1 kilometer = _1,000_ meters

6. Write the quotients. 2 each (16)

÷	72	16	40	88	48	32	64	8
8	9	2	5	11	6	4	8	1

Lesson 66 — 3 min.

Reduce.

$\frac{2}{4} = \frac{1}{2}$ $\frac{3}{6} = \frac{1}{2}$ $\frac{2}{8} = \frac{1}{4}$

$\frac{3}{9} = \frac{1}{3}$ $\frac{4}{10} = \frac{2}{5}$ $\frac{3}{15} = \frac{1}{5}$

$\frac{4}{8} = \frac{1}{2}$ $\frac{5}{10} = \frac{1}{2}$ $\frac{6}{12} = \frac{1}{2}$

$\frac{6}{9} = \frac{2}{3}$ $\frac{2}{10} = \frac{1}{5}$ $\frac{5}{15} = \frac{1}{3}$

Lesson 68 — 2 min.

Circle proper fractions and underline improper fractions.

$\frac{1}{2}$ $\frac{3}{4}$ $\frac{6}{7}$ $\frac{7}{6}$ $\frac{9}{8}$ $\frac{12}{13}$ $\frac{2}{3}$ $\frac{6}{5}$ $\frac{4}{3}$

$\frac{97}{100}$ $\frac{56}{55}$ $\frac{2}{9}$ $\frac{3}{8}$ $\frac{6}{4}$ $\frac{9}{10}$ $\frac{11}{12}$ $\frac{13}{14}$

$\frac{8}{9}$ $\frac{4}{5}$ $\frac{7}{3}$ $\frac{9}{5}$ $\frac{6}{10}$ $\frac{7}{12}$ $\frac{11}{4}$ $\frac{14}{15}$ $\frac{9}{2}$

Lesson 69 — 5 min.

+	12	8	9	11	15	7
3	15	11	12	14	18	10
13	25	21	22	24	28	20
6	18	14	15	17	21	13
7	19	15	16	18	22	14
20	32	28	29	31	35	27

Lesson 70 — 3 min.

__3__ feet = 1 yard

__1,000__ meters = 1 kilometer

__16__ ounces = 1 pound

__4__ quarts = 1 gallon

$6\overline{)5,329}$ 888 r. 1

$42\overline{)7,770}$ 185

$25\overline{)400}$ 16

Name _____

Lesson	Score
66	
68	
69	
70	

Quiz 7

Name _____ Date _____

1. Write the answers. 5 each (50)

a. 1 pound = __16__ ounces   **b.** 1 foot = __12__ inches

c. 1 year = __365__ days   **d.** 1 quart = __2__ pints

e. 1 leap year = __366__ days   **f.** 1 gallon = __4__ quarts

g. 1 ton = __2,000__ pounds   **h.** 1 decade = __10__ years

i. 1 year = __12__ months   **j.** 1 yard = __3__ feet

2. Follow the signs. 5 each (35)

a.
```
  6,908
- 5,896
-------
  1,012
```

b.
```
   2,035
×     63
--------
   6105
+ 12210
--------
 128,205
```

c.
```
 6 9
 2 3
 7 4
+3 5
----
 201
```

d.
```
  1,479
×      8
--------
 11,832
```

e.
```
 2 1/8
 2 3/8
+5 3/8
------
 9 7/8
```

f.
```
  9 11/13
- 4  5/13
---------
  5  6/13
```

g.
```
       × 36 r.7
  40 | 1,447
      -1 20↓
      -----
        247
       -240
       ----
          7
```

3. Write + or − in each blank. 5 each (15)

a. $\frac{5}{17}$ __+__ $\frac{2}{17}$ = $\frac{7}{17}$

b. $\frac{9}{11}$ __−__ $\frac{3}{11}$ = $\frac{6}{11}$

c. $\frac{3}{8}$ __+__ $\frac{2}{8}$ = $\frac{5}{8}$

Lesson 71 — 2 min.

×	5	8	6	12	4	9
10	50	80	60	120	40	90
7	35	56	42	84	28	63
2	10	16	12	24	8	18
9	45	72	54	108	36	81
11	55	88	66	132	44	99

Lesson 73 — 3 min.

```
  934        $ 14.21          32,642
  689          68.42        + 87,998
+ 256          19.27        ─────────
───────      + 29.56         120,640
 1,879       ────────
             $ 131.46
```

```
    478         9,320             27
  × 265         ×    8          × 46
─────────      ────────        ───────
 126,670        74,560          1,242
```

Lesson 74 — 5 min.

```
      1,464            42
   ┌────────        ┌──────
  5│ 7,320          6│ 252
```

```
  9,327        $ 43.09          93           21
  ×    6       − 16.87        + 68         × 56
─────────      ────────      ──────       ───────
 55,962        $ 26.22         161         1,176
```

$\frac{1}{5}$ of 10 = __2__ $\frac{1}{9}$ of 18 = __2__

Lesson 75 — 2 min.

×	2	4	6	8	10	12
12	24	48	72	96	120	144
11	22	44	66	88	110	132
10	20	40	60	80	100	120
9	18	36	54	72	90	108
8	16	32	48	64	80	96

Quiz 10 each

Lesson	Score
71	
73	
74	
75	

Test 7

Name _____ Date _____

1. Solve each story problem. Do your work on this test sheet. 3 each (6)

   a. James bought 15 folders at 19¢ each.
      How much did James pay? $2.85

   b. Max spent $1.94. How much change
      will he get back from $5.00? $3.06

2. Fill in the blanks. 2 each (14)

   a. 1 year = __365__ days

   b. 3 feet = __1__ yard

   c. 14 days = __2__ weeks

   d. 2 pints = __1__ quart

   e. 1 decade = __10__ years

   f. 1 year = about __52__ weeks

   g. 24 months = __2__ years

3. Write two factors for each. 1 each (16)
Answers will vary.

   a. 63 _____ _____

   b. 48 _____ _____

   c. 35 _____ _____

   d. 72 _____ _____

   e. 24 _____ _____

   f. 36 _____ _____

   g. 12 _____ _____

   h. 56 _____ _____

4. Add or subtract. Reduce if necessary. Show your work below each problem.
2 each (10)

  a. $\;\;5\frac{1}{4}$
   $+\,6\frac{1}{4}$
   $\overline{11\frac{1}{2}}$

  b. $\;\;7\frac{3}{8}$
   $+\,9\frac{3}{8}$
   $\overline{16\frac{3}{4}}$

  c. $\;26\frac{3}{5}$
   $+\,17\frac{1}{5}$
   $\overline{43\frac{4}{5}}$

  d. $\;35\frac{4}{5}$
   $-\,12\frac{1}{5}$
   $\overline{23\frac{3}{5}}$

  e. $\;18\frac{5}{8}$
   $-\,9\frac{3}{8}$
   $\overline{9\frac{1}{4}}$

He that getteth wisdom loveth his own soul; he that keepeth understanding shall find good. —Prov. 19:8

5. Divide and check. 2 each part (12)

a. $12\overline{)3,910}$ $\quad 325$ r. 10

$$\begin{array}{r} 325 \\ \times 12 \\ \hline 650 \\ +325 \\ \hline 3,900 \\ +\ \ 10 \\ \hline 3,910 \end{array}$$

b. $34\overline{)2,079}$ $\quad 61$ r. 5

$$\begin{array}{r} 61 \\ \times 34 \\ \hline 244 \\ +183 \\ \hline 2,074 \\ +\ \ \ 5 \\ \hline 2,079 \end{array}$$

c. $23\overline{)1,794}$ $\quad 78$

$$\begin{array}{r} 78 \\ \times 23 \\ \hline 234 \\ +156 \\ \hline 1,794 \end{array}$$

6. Follow the signs. 2 each (10)

a.
$$\begin{array}{r} 597 \\ 266 \\ 785 \\ +431 \\ \hline 2,079 \end{array}$$

b.
$$\begin{array}{r} 6,709 \\ \times\ \ \ 34 \\ \hline 228,106 \end{array}$$

c.
$$\begin{array}{r} 2,907 \\ -899 \\ \hline 2,008 \end{array}$$

d.
$$\begin{array}{r} 987 \\ \times\ \ 7 \\ \hline 6,909 \end{array}$$

e.
$$\begin{array}{r} 579 \\ \times 615 \\ \hline 356,085 \end{array}$$

7. Change to a mixed or whole number. 3 each (12)

a. $\frac{7}{6} = 1\frac{1}{6}$ b. $\frac{3}{2} = 1\frac{1}{2}$ c. $\frac{8}{3} = 2\frac{2}{3}$ d. $\frac{5}{2} = 2\frac{1}{2}$

8. Write the products. 1 each (20)

×	8	12	7	9	4
8	64	96	56	72	32
9	72	108	63	81	36
12	96	144	84	108	48
3	24	36	21	27	12

Lesson 76 — 5 min.

$$\begin{array}{r} 9 \\ \times 8 \\ \hline 72 \end{array} \qquad \begin{array}{r} 7 \\ \times 6 \\ \hline 42 \end{array} \qquad \begin{array}{r} 12 \\ \times 11 \\ \hline 132 \end{array} \qquad \begin{array}{r} 4 \\ \times 5 \\ \hline 20 \end{array} \qquad \begin{array}{r} 8 \\ \times 6 \\ \hline 48 \end{array}$$

$16 \div 8 = \underline{2}$ $\qquad$ $42 \div 7 = \underline{6}$

$36 \div 9 = \underline{4}$ $\qquad$ $56 \div 8 = \underline{7}$

$54 \div 9 = \underline{6}$ $\qquad$ $72 \div 6 = \underline{12}$

$$\begin{array}{r} 27 \\ +5 \\ \hline 32 \end{array} \qquad \begin{array}{r} 13 \\ +6 \\ \hline 19 \end{array} \qquad \begin{array}{r} 18 \\ +9 \\ \hline 27 \end{array} \qquad \begin{array}{r} 15 \\ +6 \\ \hline 21 \end{array} \qquad \begin{array}{r} 23 \\ +18 \\ \hline 41 \end{array}$$

Quiz 5 each

Lesson 78 — 3 min.

Average.

$$\begin{array}{l} 78 \\ 94 \\ 67 \\ 79 \\ 82 \end{array} \qquad \begin{array}{r} \$14.87 \\ 5.29 \\ 3.67 \\ 11.13 \end{array} \qquad \begin{array}{l} 439 \\ 687 \\ 914 \end{array}$$

4/\$34.96/\$8.74

3/2,040/680

5/400/80

Lesson 79 — 3 min.

Match.

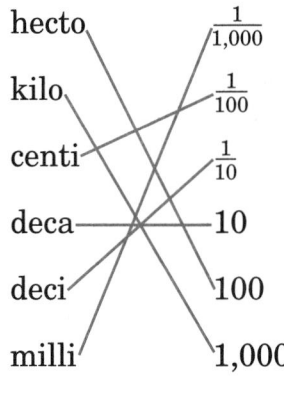

hecto $\qquad$ $\frac{1}{1,000}$

kilo $\qquad$ $\frac{1}{100}$

centi $\qquad$ $\frac{1}{10}$

deca $\qquad$ 10

deci $\qquad$ 100

milli $\qquad$ 1,000

Reduce.

$\frac{4}{8} = \frac{1}{2}$

$\frac{3}{9} = \frac{1}{3}$

$\frac{10}{12} = \frac{5}{6}$

$\frac{7}{14} = \frac{1}{2}$

$\frac{2}{6} = \frac{1}{3}$

$\frac{3}{12} = \frac{1}{4}$

$\frac{6}{10} = \frac{3}{5}$

Lesson 80 — 3 min.

+	11	9	6	17	4	12
10	21	19	16	27	14	22
9	20	18	15	26	13	21
12	23	21	18	29	16	24
5	16	14	11	22	9	17
3	14	12	9	20	7	15

Lesson	Score
76	
78	
79	
80	

Quiz 8

Name _____ Date _____

1. Choose the factor that goes with the product. 3 each (18)

	product	factor
a.	_8_ 32	5
b.	_13_ 26	19
c.	_19_ 19	7
d.	_5_ 15	8
e.	_7_ 21	9
f.	_9_ 54	13

2. Write the answers. 3 each (18)

a. 1 bushel = __4__ pecks

b. 1 year = about __52__ weeks

c. 1 quart = __2__ pints

d. 1 foot = __12__ inches

e. 1 pound = __16__ ounces

f. 1 peck = __8__ quarts

3. Circle proper fractions and box improper fractions. 3 each (21)

$\frac{5}{8}$ $\boxed{\frac{4}{3}}$ $\boxed{\frac{6}{5}}$ $\frac{4}{5}$ $\frac{2}{9}$ $\frac{3}{7}$ $\boxed{\frac{8}{5}}$

4. Reduce to lowest terms. 5 each (20)

a. $\frac{3}{6} = \frac{1}{2}$ **b.** $\frac{7}{14} = \frac{1}{2}$ **c.** $\frac{4}{6} = \frac{2}{3}$ **d.** $\frac{6}{8} = \frac{3}{4}$

5. Change to a mixed or whole number. 5 each (20)

a. $\frac{20}{4} = 5$ **b.** $\frac{7}{6} = 1\frac{1}{6}$ **c.** $\frac{48}{6} = 8$ **d.** $\frac{21}{2} = 10\frac{1}{2}$

Lesson 81 — 3 min.

Make fractions equivalent.

$\frac{4}{5} = \frac{12}{15}$ $\frac{2}{7} = \frac{6}{21}$ $\frac{3}{4} = \frac{9}{12}$

$\frac{4}{9} = \frac{8}{18}$ $\frac{6}{7} = \frac{42}{49}$ $\frac{3}{8} = \frac{6}{16}$

$\frac{5}{6} = \frac{25}{30}$ $\frac{2}{3} = \frac{16}{24}$ $\frac{7}{8} = \frac{49}{56}$

$\frac{5}{8} = \frac{10}{16}$ $\frac{3}{5} = \frac{15}{25}$ $\frac{2}{9} = \frac{14}{63}$

Lesson 83 — 3 min.

$$\begin{array}{r} 698 \\ \times\,432 \\ \hline 301,536 \end{array} \qquad \begin{array}{r} 162 \\ \times\,138 \\ \hline 22,356 \end{array} \qquad \begin{array}{r} 576 \\ \times\,249 \\ \hline 143,424 \end{array}$$

$$63\,\overline{)1,978} \quad = 31\ r.25 \qquad\qquad 54\,\overline{)2,970} \quad = 55$$

Lesson 84 — 3 min.

$$\begin{array}{r} 17\frac{2}{6} \\ 16\frac{4}{6} \\ +\,19\frac{1}{6} \\ \hline 53\frac{1}{6} \end{array} \qquad \begin{array}{r} \frac{2}{8} \\ \frac{7}{8} \\ +\,\frac{2}{8} \\ \hline 1\frac{3}{8} \end{array} \qquad \begin{array}{r} 603\frac{8}{16} \\ -\,492\frac{4}{16} \\ \hline 111\frac{1}{4} \end{array}$$

_____3_____ ft. = 1 yd. _____100_____ cm = 1 m

____24____ hr. = 1 da. _____4_____ pk. = 1 bu.

____36____ in. = 1 yd. ___5,280___ ft. = 1 mi.

____12____ mo. = 1 yr. ____16____ oz. = 1 lb.

Lesson 85 — 5 min.

×	12	6	4	10	9	11
8	96	48	32	80	72	88
9	108	54	36	90	81	99
0	0	0	0	0	0	0
5	60	30	20	50	45	55
11	132	66	44	110	99	121

Quiz 3 each

Lesson	Score
81	
83	
84	
85	

Test 8

Name _____ Date _____

1. Solve these story problems. Do your work on this test sheet. 3 each (6)

a. Joseph had a board $5\frac{3}{4}$ feet long. He sawed off a piece $1\frac{1}{4}$ feet long. How long was the piece that was left?
$4\frac{1}{2}$ ft.

b. Allison had these grades in math: 88, 92, 86, 82, 87. What was Allison's average grade?   87

2. Fill in the blanks. 3 each (21)

a. 1 ton = __2,000__ pounds

b. 1 quart = __2__ pints

c. 1 mile = __5,280__ feet

d. 1 pound = __16__ ounces

e. 1 decade = __10__ years

f. 1 week = __7__ days

g. 1 year = about __52__ weeks

3. Solve. 1 each (4)

a. 5 yards = __15__ feet

b. 2 days = __48__ hours

c. 2 centuries = __200__ years

d. 6 weeks = __42__ days

4. Add or subtract. Final answers should be written correctly. 2 each (10)

a. $\begin{array}{r}\frac{3}{8}\\[2pt]\frac{1}{8}\\[2pt]+\frac{5}{8}\\\hline 1\frac{1}{8}\end{array}$

b. $\begin{array}{r}5\frac{7}{12}\\[2pt]+1\frac{1}{12}\\\hline 6\frac{2}{3}\end{array}$

c. $\begin{array}{r}2\frac{3}{4}\\[2pt]-1\frac{1}{4}\\\hline 1\frac{1}{2}\end{array}$

d. $\begin{array}{r}3\frac{3}{10}\\[2pt]2\frac{7}{10}\\[2pt]+1\frac{1}{10}\\\hline 7\frac{1}{10}\end{array}$

e. $\begin{array}{r}2\frac{15}{16}\\[2pt]-1\frac{7}{16}\\\hline 1\frac{1}{2}\end{array}$

No man is born into the world whose work is not born with him.—There is always work, and tools to work with, for those who will. —James Russell Lowell

5. Write *P* if proper or *I* if improper. 3 each (15)

a. __I__ $\frac{3}{2}$ b. __P__ $\frac{7}{8}$ c. __I__ $\frac{4}{4}$ d. __I__ $\frac{7}{2}$ e. __P__ $\frac{3}{4}$

6. Divide and check. 2 each step (12)

a.
$$33\overline{)693} \quad \frac{21}{21}$$
$$\begin{array}{r} 21 \\ \times 33 \\ \hline 63 \\ +63 \\ \hline 693 \end{array}$$

b.
$$84\overline{)1{,}260} \quad 15$$
$$\begin{array}{r} 15 \\ \times 84 \\ \hline 60 \\ +120 \\ \hline 1{,}260 \end{array}$$

c.
$$71\overline{)1{,}766} \quad 24\,r.62$$
$$\begin{array}{r} 24 \\ \times 71 \\ \hline 24 \\ +168 \\ \hline 1704 \\ +\;\;\;62 \\ \hline 1{,}766 \end{array}$$

7. Follow the signs. 2 each (10)

a.
$$\begin{array}{r} 4{,}247 \\ 2{,}674 \\ 1{,}879 \\ +2{,}346 \\ \hline 11{,}146 \end{array}$$

b.
$$\begin{array}{r} 3{,}045 \\ -1{,}549 \\ \hline 1{,}496 \end{array}$$

c.
$$\begin{array}{r} 1{,}932 \\ \times\;\;\;26 \\ \hline 50{,}232 \end{array}$$

d.
$$\begin{array}{r} 479 \\ \times 179 \\ \hline 85{,}741 \end{array}$$

e.
$$\begin{array}{r} 21 \\ 37 \\ +24 \\ \hline 82 \end{array}$$

8. Reduce to lowest terms. 3 each (18)

a. $\frac{6}{8} = \frac{3}{4}$ b. $\frac{2}{4} = \frac{1}{2}$ c. $\frac{4}{8} = \frac{1}{2}$

d. $\frac{5}{15} = \frac{1}{3}$ e. $\frac{10}{14} = \frac{5}{7}$ f. $\frac{3}{6} = \frac{1}{2}$

9. Give the least common multiple of these numbers. 1 each (4)

a. 2, 4, 6   b. 3, 9, 2   c. 3, 6, 4   d. 2, 3

__12__   __18__   __12__   __6__

Lesson 86 — 5 min.

$$
\begin{array}{r}
9\,7\,2 \\
\times\ \ 6 \\
\hline
5,8\,3\,2
\end{array}
\qquad
\begin{array}{r}
2,3\,5\,8 \\
\times\ \ \ \ 9 \\
\hline
2\,1,2\,2\,2
\end{array}
\qquad
\begin{array}{r}
4\,3\,8 \\
\times\ \ 2 \\
\hline
8\,7\,6
\end{array}
$$

$$
\begin{array}{r}
\$1\,3.6\,2 \\
-\ \ 4.9\,7 \\
\hline
\$8.6\,5
\end{array}
\qquad
\begin{array}{r}
2,3\,0\,6 \\
-1,4\,0\,9 \\
\hline
8\,9\,7
\end{array}
\qquad
\begin{array}{r}
1,6\,0\,0 \\
-\ \ 8\,7\,6 \\
\hline
7\,2\,4
\end{array}
$$

$$
5\overline{)6\,5}\ \ ^{1\,3}
\qquad
4\overline{)3\,6}\ \ ^{9}
\qquad
9\overline{)1\,8}\ \ ^{2}
$$

Quiz 8 each

Lesson 88 — 2 min. 30 sec.

XXIX = __29__   XIV = __14__
MDV = _1,505_   CX = __110__
LXXI = __71__   XXXIII = __33__
MDC = _1,600_   CCCXX = __320__
LV = __55__   III = __3__
XII = __12__   XL = __40__

3 ft. = __36__ in.   7 weeks = __49__ days

Lesson 89 — 2 min.

$9 + 8 + 4 + 5 + 6 =$ __32__
$16 - 5 + 3 + 2 - 4 =$ __12__
$3 + 5 + 4 + 6 + 8 =$ __26__
$27 - 9 + 4 + 5 + 2 =$ __29__
$74 + 6 + 20 - 50 =$ __50__
$23 + 17 + 10 - 3 =$ __47__
$21 + 9 + 5 + 7 + 3 =$ __45__
$14 + 7 + 6 + 5 - 2 =$ __30__
$5 + 9 + 6 + 10 + 3 =$ __33__
$8 + 9 - 3 + 2 - 4 - 1 =$ __11__
$62 + 5 - 7 + 9 =$ __69__
$31 + 5 + 6 + 2 =$ __44__

Lesson 90 — 2 min. 30 sec.

×	7	3	6	9	11	8
12	84	36	72	108	132	96
9	63	27	54	81	99	72
10	70	30	60	90	110	80
4	28	12	24	36	44	32
2	14	6	12	18	22	16

Lesson	Score
86	
88	
89	
90	

Quiz 9

Name _____ Date _____

1. Write the correct numbers. 5 each (60)

a. $\frac{1}{4} = \frac{3}{12}$ b. $\frac{3}{4} = \frac{12}{16}$ c. $\frac{2}{3} = \frac{16}{24}$ d. $\frac{5}{6} = \frac{15}{18}$

e. $V = \underline{5}$ f. $X = \underline{10}$ g. $L = \underline{50}$ h. $C = \underline{100}$

i. $D = \underline{500}$ j. $9 \times 6 = \underline{54}$ k. $15 - 7 = \underline{8}$ l. $18 + 9 = \underline{27}$

2. Follow the signs. 5 each (30)

a.
$$\begin{array}{r} 2\,7 \\ 3\,2 \\ 5\,6 \\ +\,4\,9 \\ \hline 1\,6\,4 \end{array}$$

b.
$$\begin{array}{r} 3\,2\,1 \\ -\,2\,8\,7 \\ \hline 3\,4 \end{array}$$

c.
$$\begin{array}{r} 3\,5\,9 \\ \times\,8\,1 \\ \hline 3\,5\,9 \\ +\,2\,8\,7\,2 \\ \hline 2\,9,0\,7\,9 \end{array}$$

d.
$$\begin{array}{r} \frac{3}{11} \\ \frac{2}{11} \\ +\,\frac{4}{11} \\ \hline \frac{9}{11} \end{array}$$

e.
$$\begin{array}{r} 3\frac{3}{8} = \ \ 3\frac{3}{8} \\ +\,2\frac{1}{2} = +\,2\frac{4}{8} \\ \hline 5\frac{7}{8} \end{array}$$

f.
$$\begin{array}{r} 3\,1\,\text{r.}\,3\,0 \\ 5\,0\,\overline{)\,1,5\,8\,0} \\ -\,1\,5\,0\!\downarrow \\ \hline 8\,0 \\ -\,5\,0 \\ \hline 3\,0 \end{array}$$

3. Reduce to lowest terms. 5 each (10)

a. $\frac{5}{15} = \underline{\frac{1}{3}}$ b. $\frac{3}{12} = \underline{\frac{1}{4}}$

$1 = \frac{6}{6}$ $1 = \frac{9}{9}$ $1 = \frac{8}{8}$ $1 = \frac{3}{3}$

$1 = \frac{5}{5}$ $1 = \frac{12}{12}$ $1 = \frac{4}{4}$ $1 = \frac{2}{2}$

$1 = \frac{7}{7}$ $1 = \frac{11}{11}$

$$5\frac{1}{2} - 1\frac{1}{4} = 4\frac{1}{4}$$

$$6\frac{1}{3} - 6\frac{1}{5} = \frac{2}{15}$$

$$\frac{6}{11} - \frac{4}{11} = \frac{2}{11}$$

Write the Roman numeral for each.

23   XXIII   1,013   MXIII

76   LXXVI   290   CCXC

14   XIV   56   LVI

17   XVII   2,222   MMCCXXII

16   XVI   50   L

5   V   90   XC

Reduce.

$\frac{2}{4} = \frac{1}{2}$ $\frac{3}{9} = \frac{1}{3}$ $\frac{4}{12} = \frac{1}{3}$ $\frac{6}{10} = \frac{3}{5}$

+	14	7	9	11	16	5
10	24	17	19	21	26	15
8	22	15	17	19	24	13
6	20	13	15	17	22	11
11	25	18	20	22	27	16
4	18	11	13	15	20	9

$$\begin{array}{r} \$3.97 \\ -2.99 \\ \hline \$.98 \end{array}$$

$$\begin{array}{r} \$29.87 \\ +42.95 \\ \hline \$72.82 \end{array}$$

$$\begin{array}{r} \$3.91 \\ \times \quad 6 \\ \hline \$23.46 \end{array}$$

$$\frac{6}{8} + \frac{3}{4} = 1\frac{1}{2}$$

$$1\frac{1}{2} + 3\frac{2}{4} = 5$$

$$\frac{9}{11} - \frac{4}{11} = \frac{5}{11}$$

Quiz 10 each

Lesson	Score
91	
93	
94	
95	

Test 9

Name _____ Date _____

1. Fill in the blanks. 2 each (16)

    a. $\frac{3}{4} = \frac{12}{16}$ **b.** $\frac{4}{5} = \frac{20}{25}$ **c.** $\frac{5}{9} = \frac{15}{27}$ **d.** $\frac{11}{12} = \frac{22}{24}$

    e. $\frac{2}{5} = \frac{6}{15}$ **f.** $\frac{3}{8} = \frac{24}{64}$ **g.** $\frac{1}{7} = \frac{2}{14}$ **h.** $\frac{2}{7} = \frac{6}{21}$

2. Match by putting the correct Arabic numeral in the blank. 2 each (20)

    a. __5__ V   1

    b. __50__ L   1,980

    c. __1__ I   5

    d. __10__ X   10

    e. __100__ C   202

    f. __1,000__ M   176

    g. __500__ D   500

    h. __176__ CLXXVI   50

    i. __202__ CCII   1,000

    j. __1,980__ MCMLXXX   100

3. Divide and check. 2 each part (12)

    a. $8\overline{)1,592}$ gives 199; $\begin{array}{r} 199 \\ \times\ 8 \\ \hline 1,592 \end{array}$

    b. $21\overline{)9,261}$ gives 441; $\begin{array}{r} 441 \\ \times\ 21 \\ \hline 9,261 \end{array}$

    c. $62\overline{)43,462}$ gives 701; $\begin{array}{r} 701 \\ \times\ 62 \\ \hline 43,462 \end{array}$

Do little things now; so shall big things come to thee by and by asking to be done. —Persian Proverb

4. *Circle* **improper fractions and** *box* **proper fractions.** 3 each (21)

$\boxed{\dfrac{5}{6}}$
$\enclose{circle}{\dfrac{16}{3}}$
$\enclose{circle}{\dfrac{15}{12}}$
$\boxed{\dfrac{3}{4}}$
$\enclose{circle}{\dfrac{7}{6}}$
$\enclose{circle}{\dfrac{50}{49}}$
$\enclose{circle}{\dfrac{27}{15}}$

5. Fill in the blanks. 1 each (16)

a. $9 \times 8 =$ ___72___ **b.** $7 \times 5 =$ ___35___

c. $7 \times 9 =$ ___63___ **d.** $6 \times 8 =$ ___48___

e. $8 \times 7 =$ ___56___ **f.** $4 \times 7 =$ ___28___

g. $4 \times 9 =$ ___36___ **h.** $7 \times 7 =$ ___49___

i. $9 \times 6 =$ ___54___ **j.** $7 \times 6 =$ ___42___

k. $5 \times 7 =$ ___35___ **l.** $3 \times 9 =$ ___27___

m. $6 \times 3 =$ ___18___ **n.** $8 \times 4 =$ ___32___

o. $8 \times 8 =$ ___64___ **p.** $7 \times 6 =$ ___42___

6. Follow the signs. 3 each (15)

a.
$$\begin{array}{r} 47 \\ 26 \\ 39 \\ +45 \\ \hline 157 \end{array}$$

b.
$$\begin{array}{r} 6\frac{3}{4} \\ +2\frac{1}{2} \\ \hline 9\frac{1}{4} \end{array}$$

c.
$$\begin{array}{r} 3,076 \\ -1,893 \\ \hline 1,183 \end{array}$$

d.
$$\begin{array}{r} 13\frac{4}{5} \\ -9\frac{1}{10} \\ \hline 4\frac{7}{10} \end{array}$$

e.
$$\begin{array}{r} 392 \\ \times 407 \\ \hline 159,544 \end{array}$$

Lesson 96 — 3 min.

$$468 \times 249 = 116{,}532$$

$$687 \times 158 = 108{,}546$$

$$209 \times 350 = 73{,}150$$

$$23\overline{)987} = 42 \text{ r.} 21$$

$$48\overline{)3{,}296} = 68 \text{ r.} 32$$

Lesson 98 — 3 min.

$$1 - \frac{2}{5} = \frac{3}{5}$$

$$1 - \frac{4}{9} = \frac{5}{9}$$

$$1 - \frac{3}{8} = \frac{5}{8}$$

$$1 - \frac{6}{7} = \frac{1}{7}$$

$$6 - 3\frac{2}{5} = 2\frac{3}{5}$$

$$8 - 6\frac{1}{2} = 1\frac{1}{2}$$

$$5 - 1\frac{1}{7} = 3\frac{6}{7}$$

$$4 - 2\frac{2}{9} = 1\frac{7}{9}$$

Lesson 99 — 3 min.

$$956 + 872 + 523 = 2{,}351$$

$$\$.67 + .29 + .35 = \$1.31$$

$$\frac{5}{11} + \frac{3}{11} + \frac{2}{11} = \frac{10}{11}$$

$$\frac{3}{9} + \frac{3}{9} = \frac{2}{3}$$

$$\frac{2}{6} + \frac{1}{3} = \frac{2}{3}$$

$$\frac{3}{5} + \frac{1}{15} = \frac{2}{3}$$

Lesson 100 — 5 min.

- __3__ ft. = 1 yd.
- __2__ pt. = 1 qt.
- __36__ in. = 1 yd.
- __8__ qt. = 1 pk.
- __100__ yr. = 1 century
- __366__ da. = 1 leap yr.
- __24__ hr. = 1 da.
- __100__ g = 1 hg
- __1,000__ m = 1 km
- __2,000__ lb. = 1 ton
- __4__ pk. = 1 bu.
- __7__ da. = 1 wk.

Quiz 8 each

Lesson	Score
96	
98	
99	
100	

Quiz 10

Name _____ Date _____

1. Write the answers. 4 each (32)

   a. 1 decade = __10__ yr.

   b. 1 lb. = __16__ oz.

   c. 1 gal. = __4__ qt.

   d. 1 mi. = __5,280__ ft.

   e. 1 ft. = __12__ in.

   f. 1 bu. = __4__ pk.

   g. 1 yd. = __3__ ft.

   h. 1 da. = __24__ hr.

2. Write the missing factors. 4 each (32)

   a. $12 \times \underline{6} = 72$

   b. $9 \times \underline{9} = 81$

   c. $12 \times \underline{7} = 84$

   d. $12 \times \underline{9} = 108$

   e. $8 \times \underline{8} = 64$

   f. $7 \times \underline{7} = 49$

   g. $6 \times \underline{9} = 54$

   h. $12 \times \underline{4} = 48$

3. Reduce. 5 each (15)

   a. $\frac{4}{8} = \frac{1}{2}$ **b.** $\frac{3}{9} = \frac{1}{3}$ **c.** $\frac{4}{6} = \frac{2}{3}$

4. Divide. 5

$$
\begin{array}{r}
84 \\
13\overline{\smash{)}1{,}092} \\
-104 \\
\hline
52 \\
-52 \\
\hline
0
\end{array}
$$

5. Subtract. 5 each (15)

   a.
$$
\begin{array}{r}
394 \\
-122 \\
\hline
272
\end{array}
$$

   b.
$$
\begin{array}{r}
7{,}000 \\
-2{,}684 \\
\hline
4{,}316
\end{array}
$$

   c.
$$
\begin{array}{r}
1 \\
-\frac{3}{4} \\
\hline
\frac{1}{4}
\end{array}
$$

Lesson 101　　2 min.

×	10	9	12	6	3	8
7	70	63	84	42	21	56
5	50	45	60	30	15	40
9	90	81	108	54	27	72
12	120	108	144	72	36	96
11	110	99	132	66	33	88

Lesson 103　　3 min.

Average.

```
5 3 2        $ 9 3. 1 8        9 5
6 8 1        $ 7 6. 0 8        8 7
5 1 5        $ 8 5. 9 2        9 3
7 8 2        $ 7 0. 7 0        9 0
                               8 0
627 r. 2      $81.47           5 5

                               83 r. 2
```

Lesson 104　　3 min.

```
   1 9 7        3 2 1        9 5 1
 × 2 4 6      × 6 0 2      × 8 7 6
4 8, 4 6 2   1 9 3, 2 4 2  8 3 3, 0 7 6
```

```
       2 1 7 r. 8          2 7 1 r. 2 9
2 4 | 5, 2 1 6       3 2 | 8, 7 0 1
```

Lesson 105　　5 min.

×	7	4	11	8	3	9
5	35	20	55	40	15	45
8	56	32	88	64	24	72
6	42	24	66	48	18	54
11	77	44	121	88	33	99
7	49	28	77	56	21	63

Quiz 3 each

Lesson	Score
101	
103	
104	
105	

Test 10

Name _____ Date _____

1. **Match by putting the correct Arabic numeral in the blank.** 2 each (20)

   a. _1,505_ MDV   601
   b. __601__ DCI   1,505
   c. __160__ CLX   42
   d. __42__ XLII   2,111
   e. __39__ XXXIX   110
   f. __110__ CX   39
   g. _2,111_ MMCXI   18
   h. _1,015_ MXV   67
   i. __67__ LXVII   160
   j. __18__ XVIII   1,015

2. **Fill in the blanks with the correct numbers.** 1 each (12)

   a. $1 = \frac{5}{5}$

   b. $1 = \frac{7}{7}$

   c. $1 = \frac{9}{9}$

   d. $6 = 5\frac{2}{2}$

   e. $7 = 6\frac{3}{3}$

   f. $4 = 3\frac{10}{10}$

   g. $\frac{2}{3} = \frac{4}{6}$

   h. $\frac{4}{5} = \frac{12}{15}$

   i. $\frac{1}{7} = \frac{4}{28}$

   j. $\frac{3}{4} = \frac{12}{16}$

   k. $\frac{2}{9} = \frac{12}{54}$

   l. $\frac{7}{8} = \frac{21}{24}$

3. **Subtract carefully.** 2 each (8)

   a. $\begin{array}{r} 1 \\ -\frac{2}{3} \\ \hline \frac{1}{3} \end{array}$

   b. $\begin{array}{r} 5 \\ -\frac{7}{8} \\ \hline 4\frac{1}{8} \end{array}$

   c. $\begin{array}{r} 3\frac{2}{7} \\ -1\frac{5}{7} \\ \hline 1\frac{4}{7} \end{array}$

   d. $\begin{array}{r} 7\frac{1}{12} \\ -3\frac{1}{6} \\ \hline 3\frac{11}{12} \end{array}$

Those who labor in the earth are the chosen people of God. —Thomas Jefferson

4. Add correctly. 2 each (10)

a. $1\frac{1}{5}$

$+1\frac{1}{2}$

$2\frac{7}{10}$

b. $6\frac{1}{3}$

$+7\frac{1}{2}$

$13\frac{5}{6}$

c. $7\frac{1}{3}$

$+5\frac{1}{6}$

$12\frac{1}{2}$

d $3\frac{3}{4}$

$2\frac{1}{2}$

$+2\frac{3}{4}$

9

e. $1\frac{3}{4}$

$1\frac{3}{4}$

$+1\frac{1}{3}$

$4\frac{5}{6}$

5. Write the products to the 12 multiplication table. 2 each (28)

0×12	1×12	2×12	3×12	4×12	5×12
0	12	24	36	48	60

6×12	7×12	8×12	9×12	10×12	11×12
72	84	96	108	120	132

12×12

144

6. Change these to mixed or whole numbers. 2 each (10)

a. $\frac{3}{2} = 1\frac{1}{2}$ b. $\frac{7}{4} = 1\frac{3}{4}$ c. $\frac{11}{6} = 1\frac{5}{6}$ d. $\frac{10}{5} = 2$ e. $\frac{5}{3} = 1\frac{2}{3}$

7. Divide and check. 2 each part (12)

a. $\begin{array}{r} 37 \\ 41\overline{)1,517} \end{array}$ $\begin{array}{r} 37 \\ \times 41 \\ \hline 1,517 \end{array}$

b. $\begin{array}{r} 25 \\ 37\overline{)925} \end{array}$ $\begin{array}{r} 25 \\ \times 37 \\ \hline 925 \end{array}$

c. $\begin{array}{r} 507\,r.5 \\ 8\overline{)4,061} \end{array}$ $\begin{array}{r} 507 \\ \times 8 \\ \hline 4,056 \\ + 5 \\ \hline 4,061 \end{array}$

M = 1,000   CM = 900

D = 500   CD = 400

I = 1   XI = 11

V = 5   XV = 15

C = 100   XC = 90

MX = 1,010   VIII = 8

DX = 510   CX = 110

IX = 9

$\frac{1}{11}$ of 55 = 5 $\frac{1}{10}$ of 120 = 12

$\frac{1}{9}$ of 81 = 9 $\frac{1}{4}$ of 16 = 4

Change to mixed numbers.

$\frac{17}{8} = 2\frac{1}{8}$ $\frac{16}{5} = 3\frac{1}{5}$ $\frac{12}{7} = 1\frac{5}{7}$

$\frac{32}{9} = 3\frac{5}{9}$ $\frac{18}{5} = 3\frac{3}{5}$ $\frac{41}{10} = 4\frac{1}{10}$

$\frac{35}{6} = 5\frac{5}{6}$ $\frac{54}{7} = 7\frac{5}{7}$ $\frac{11}{2} = 5\frac{1}{2}$

$\frac{27}{4} = 6\frac{3}{4}$ $\frac{31}{3} = 10\frac{1}{3}$ $\frac{49}{6} = 8\frac{1}{6}$

25 ÷ 5 = 5   8 × 4 = 32

19 + 8 = 27   27 − 6 = 21

38 + 11 = 49   9 × 9 = 81

72 ÷ 6 = 12   54 ÷ 2 = 27

7 × 6 = 42   38 − 19 = 19

138 + 22 = 160   132 ÷ 11 = 12

56 ÷ 4 = 14   18 × 3 = 54

16 × 5 = 80   12 ÷ 12 = 1

$$\begin{array}{r} 785 \\ \times 430 \\ \hline 337,550 \end{array} \qquad \begin{array}{r} 926 \\ \times 890 \\ \hline 824,140 \end{array} \qquad \begin{array}{r} 459 \\ \times 670 \\ \hline 307,530 \end{array}$$

$$47 \overline{)8,322} = 177 \text{ r. } 3 \qquad 81 \overline{)4,360} = 53 \text{ r. } 67$$

Quiz 5 each

Lesson	Score
106	
108	
109	
110	

Quiz 11

Name _____ Date _____

1. Write the answers. 3 each (36)

a. $6 \times 9 = \underline{54}$ **b.** $16 + 9 = \underline{25}$ **c.** $32 \div 4 = \underline{8}$

d. $15 \div 3 = \underline{5}$ **e.** $24 \div 3 = \underline{8}$ **f.** $17 - 8 = \underline{9}$

g. $7 + 9 = \underline{16}$ **h.** $7 \times 9 = \underline{63}$ **i.** $13 + 3 = \underline{16}$

j. $12 \times 8 = \underline{96}$ **k.** $21 - 8 = \underline{13}$ **l.** $13 - 6 = \underline{7}$

2. Change to improper fractions. 4 each (12)

a. $1\frac{1}{4} = \underline{\frac{5}{4}}$ **b.** $3\frac{2}{5} = \underline{\frac{17}{5}}$ **c.** $4\frac{5}{6} = \underline{\frac{29}{6}}$

3. Read each sentence carefully. Fill in the blanks by choosing the correct answer. 5 each (30)

whole	numerator	proper	denominator
	mixed	improper	

a. The fraction $\frac{9}{5}$ is an _____improper_____ fraction.

b. The fraction $\frac{5}{9}$ is a _____proper_____ fraction.

c. The number $1\frac{5}{9}$ is a _____mixed_____ number.

d. The number 1 is a _____whole_____ number.

e. Change $\frac{4}{3}$ to a mixed number by dividing the numerator by the _____denominator_____.

f. Change $1\frac{1}{3}$ to an improper fraction by multiplying the whole number by the denominator and adding the _____numerator_____.

4. Write the answers. 5 each (20)

a.
$$\begin{array}{r} 23 \\ \times\,47 \\ \hline 161 \\ +\,92 \\ \hline 1,081 \end{array}$$

b.
$$\begin{array}{r} \$60.29 \\ -\,42.87 \\ \hline \$17.42 \end{array}$$

c.
$$\begin{array}{r} 2\frac{3}{5} \\ +\,9\frac{1}{2} \\ \hline 12\frac{1}{10} \end{array}$$

d.
$$\begin{array}{r} \frac{6}{7} \\ -\,\frac{1}{7} \\ \hline \frac{5}{7} \end{array}$$

×	8	6	9	0	7	2
12	96	72	108	0	84	24
8	64	48	72	0	56	16
10	80	60	90	0	70	20
7	56	42	63	0	49	14
11	88	66	99	0	77	22

Average.

7 2	$ 4 2. 9 6	6 9
5 4	$ 2 7. 5 2	7 4
9 9	$ 6 5. 8 7	8 7
6 3	$ 4 5. 4 5	6 8
3 6		7 4 r. 2
1 8		
5 7		

Write the missing signs.

$6 \times 3 = 18$ $16 + 6 = 22$

$4 \times 2 = 8$ $13 - 9 = 4$

$12 \div 2 = 6$ $22 \div 11 = 2$

$27 + 4 = 31$ $35 \div 5 = 7$

$18 - 9 = 9$ $4 \times 8 = 32$

$18 \div 9 = 2$ $9 - 7 = 2$

$9 \times 3 = 27$ $54 \div 6 = 9$

+	10	5	16	12	13	9
8	18	13	24	20	21	17
4	14	9	20	16	17	13
9	19	14	25	21	22	18
6	16	11	22	18	19	15
3	13	8	19	15	16	12

Quiz 3 each

Lesson	Score
111	
113	
114	
115	

Test 11

Name _____ Date _____

1. Solve these story problems. Do your work for *b* and *c* on this test sheet.
2 each (6)

   a. The last chapter of Julie's book is marked XXVI.
How many chapters are in Julie's book? 26 chapters

   b. A fudge recipe calls for $\frac{1}{2}$ cup of cocoa.
If only $\frac{1}{2}$ of the recipe is made, how
much cocoa should be used? $\frac{1}{4}$ cup

   c. Two brothers bought a Bible which
cost \$5.78 for their mother's birthday.
They shared the cost equally. How
much did each boy pay? \$2.89

2. Find the answer. 3 each (36)

a.
$$\begin{array}{r} \frac{3}{8} \\ 2\frac{3}{4} \\ +6\frac{1}{2} \\ \hline 9\frac{5}{8} \end{array}$$

b.
$$\begin{array}{r} 11 \\ -\frac{3}{5} \\ \hline 10\frac{2}{5} \end{array}$$

c.
$$\begin{array}{r} 4\frac{2}{3} \\ -1\frac{3}{4} \\ \hline 2\frac{11}{12} \end{array}$$

d.
$$\begin{array}{r} 4\frac{1}{6} \\ 8\frac{1}{8} \\ +9\frac{1}{3} \\ \hline 21\frac{5}{8} \end{array}$$

e. $\frac{1}{2} \times \frac{1}{4} = \frac{1}{8}$

f. $\frac{1}{3} \times \frac{2}{5} = \frac{2}{15}$

g. $\frac{2}{3} \times \frac{1}{5} = \frac{2}{15}$

h. $\frac{1}{4} \times \frac{1}{4} = \frac{1}{16}$

i. $1 = \frac{5}{5}$

j. $3 = \underline{\frac{2}{2}}$

k. $\frac{3}{8} = \frac{6}{16}$

l. $\frac{5}{10} = \frac{1}{2}$

I am only one,
But still I am one.
I cannot do everything,
But still I can do something;
And because I cannot do everything
I will not refuse to do the something that I can do.
—Edward Everett Hale

3. Divide and check. 2 each part (12)

a.
$$25\overline{)2,331} \quad 93\text{ r. }6$$
$$\begin{array}{r} 93 \\ \times 25 \\ \hline 2,325 \\ + \quad 6 \\ \hline 2,331 \end{array}$$

b.
$$32\overline{)3,136} \quad 98$$
$$\begin{array}{r} 98 \\ \times 32 \\ \hline 3,136 \end{array}$$

c.
$$24\overline{)3,285} \quad 136\text{ r. }21$$
$$\begin{array}{r} 136 \\ \times 24 \\ \hline 3,264 \\ + \quad 21 \\ \hline 3,285 \end{array}$$

4. Fill in the blanks. 2 each (10)

a. __8__ Which number is the denominator in $\frac{7}{8}$?

b. __2__ Which number is the numerator in $\frac{2}{3}$?

c. __9__ What is the missing term in $\frac{3}{4} = \frac{}{12}$?

d. __no__ Does $\frac{4}{8} = \frac{8}{24}$? Write *yes* or *no*.

e. __$14\frac{1}{2}$__ Which number is a mixed number: $\frac{2}{5}$, $14\frac{1}{2}$, 72?

5. Write the products. 1 each (36)

×	8	6	11	7	4	2	12	5	9
9	72	54	99	63	36	18	108	45	81
12	96	72	132	84	48	24	144	60	108
3	24	18	33	21	12	6	36	15	27
8	64	48	88	56	32	16	96	40	72

$$9 \overline{)36} = 4 \qquad 7 \overline{)28} = 4 \qquad 6 \overline{)30} = 5 \qquad 3 \overline{)9} = 3$$

$$4 \overline{)48} = 12 \qquad 3 \overline{)27} = 9 \qquad 8 \overline{)32} = 4 \qquad 3 \overline{)18} = 6$$

$$6 \overline{)72} = 12 \qquad 9 \overline{)54} = 6 \qquad 11 \overline{)33} = 3 \qquad 6 \overline{)84} = 14$$

Quiz 5 each

$$\begin{array}{r} 325 \\ \times 406 \\ \hline 131,950 \end{array} \qquad \begin{array}{r} 578 \\ \times 250 \\ \hline 144,500 \end{array} \qquad \begin{array}{r} 145 \\ \times 270 \\ \hline 39,150 \end{array}$$

$$15 \overline{)2,730} = 182 \qquad 20 \overline{)5,000} = 250$$

×	3	6	2	12	7	4
11	33	66	22	132	77	44
8	24	48	16	96	56	32
6	18	36	12	72	42	24
10	30	60	20	120	70	40
9	27	54	18	108	63	36

×	3	9	11	5	6	7
12	36	108	132	60	72	84
9	27	81	99	45	54	63
5	15	45	55	25	30	35
8	24	72	88	40	48	56
11	33	99	121	55	66	77

Lesson	Score
116	
118	
119	
120	

Quiz 12

Name _____ Date _____

1. Write the quotients. 3 each (30)

÷	81	63	45	27	72	99	9	18	36	108
9	9	7	5	3	8	11	1	2	4	12

2. Circle the five fractions that can be reduced. 3 each (15)

$\frac{15}{20}$ $\frac{1}{3}$ $\frac{29}{30}$ $\frac{12}{72}$ $\frac{4}{10}$ $\frac{2}{8}$ $\frac{14}{16}$ $\frac{1}{5}$

3. Change to improper fractions. 5 each (15)

a. $1\frac{5}{8} = \frac{13}{8}$ b. $2\frac{3}{4} = \frac{11}{4}$ c. $6\frac{2}{5} = \frac{32}{5}$

4. Multiply. 5 each (15)

a. $\frac{1}{2} \times \frac{1}{4} = \frac{1}{8}$ b. $\frac{2}{3} \times \frac{1}{5} = \frac{2}{15}$ c. $\frac{\overset{1}{3}}{5} \times \frac{5}{\underset{2}{6}} = \frac{1}{2}$

5. Follow the signs. 5 each (25)

a.
```
   2,568
   3,056
 + 6,732
  12,356
```

b.
```
 $49.28
- 25.48
 $23.80
```

c.
```
  5,601
×     9
 50,409
```

d.
```
    23
  × 42
    46
  + 92
   966
```

e.
```
    1
  - 5/8
   3/8
```

lesson 117   **93**

Lesson 121 — 3 min.

$$39\,r.40$$
$$69\,\overline{|2,731}$$

$$165\,r.32$$
$$54\,\overline{|8,942}$$

$$6,924\,r.5$$
$$9\,\overline{|62,321}$$

$$5,189\,r.4$$
$$8\,\overline{|41,516}$$

Lesson 123 — 3 min.

Reduce if necessary.

$$\frac{1}{2} \times \frac{3}{5} = \frac{3}{10} \qquad \frac{6}{7} \times \frac{2}{3} = \frac{4}{7}$$

$$\frac{1}{5} \times \frac{1}{2} = \frac{1}{10} \qquad \frac{3}{4} \times \frac{1}{2} = \frac{3}{8}$$

$$\frac{5}{6} \times \frac{3}{5} = \frac{1}{2} \qquad \frac{3}{8} \times \frac{1}{2} = \frac{3}{16}$$

Lesson 124 — 2 min.

×	11	5	8	9	6	2
9	99	45	72	81	54	18
8	88	40	64	72	48	16
12	132	60	96	108	72	24
7	77	35	56	63	42	14
6	66	30	48	54	36	12

Lesson 125 — 5 min.

$$\begin{array}{r} 598 \\ \times 24 \\ \hline 14,352 \end{array} \qquad \begin{array}{r} 652 \\ \times 580 \\ \hline 378,160 \end{array} \qquad \begin{array}{r} 958 \\ \times 624 \\ \hline 597,792 \end{array}$$

$$\begin{array}{r} 6,392 \\ -4,487 \\ \hline 1,905 \end{array} \qquad \begin{array}{r} 283 \\ -167 \\ \hline 116 \end{array} \qquad \begin{array}{r} \$23.00 \\ -\ 9.87 \\ \hline \$13.13 \end{array}$$

Quiz 10 each

Lesson	Score
121	
123	
124	
125	

Test 12

Name _____ Date _____

1. Fill in the blanks. 2 each (30)

    a. 1 year = __365__ days   **b.** 1 gallon = __4__ quarts

    c. 1 pound = __16__ ounces   **d.** 1 gram = __100__ centigrams

    e. 1 day = __24__ hours   **f.** 1 foot = __12__ inches

    g. $54 \div 9 =$ __6__   **h.** $36 \div 12 =$ __3__

    i. $24 \div 8 =$ __3__   **j.** $18 \div 2 =$ __9__

    k. MC = __1,100__   **l.** XXIV = __24__

    m. DXC = __590__   **n.** MDCI = __1,601__

    o. III = __3__

2. Follow the signs. 2 each (16)

a.
$$\begin{array}{r} 8\,7 \\ 2\,3 \\ 4\,9 \\ +\,5\,1 \\ \hline 2\,1\,0 \end{array}$$

b.
$$\begin{array}{r} 1\,6\frac{4}{9} \\ 3\,1 \\ +\,2\,7\frac{1}{3} \\ \hline 7\,4\frac{7}{9} \end{array}$$

c.
$$\begin{array}{r} 1\,1\frac{1}{5} \\ -\,1\,0\frac{4}{15} \\ \hline \frac{14}{15} \end{array}$$

d.
$$\begin{array}{r} \$3\,6.7\,3 \\ -\,1\,9.8\,4 \\ \hline \$1\,6.8\,9 \end{array}$$

e.
$$\begin{array}{r} 9,0\,6\,2 \\ \times\quad\ 8 \\ \hline 7\,2,4\,9\,6 \end{array}$$

f. $\frac{2}{5} \times \frac{3}{7} = \frac{6}{35}$

g.
$$\begin{array}{r} 9\,0\,7 \\ \times\,3\,2\,5 \\ \hline 2\,9\,4,7\,7\,5 \end{array}$$

h. $25\overline{)7,962}$ 318 r. 12

All work, even cotton-spinning, is noble; work is alone noble. —Thomas Carlyle

3. **Write two factors for each.** 1 each (8) (Answers will vary.)

    a. 36 _____ _____   **b.** 70 _____ _____

    c. 18 _____ _____   **d.** 27 _____ _____

4. **Multiply.** 3 each (12)

    a. $\frac{3}{8} \times 42 = 15\frac{3}{4}$ **b.** $1\frac{1}{2} \times \frac{2}{3} = 1$ **c.** $6\frac{2}{3} \times \frac{3}{5} = 4$ **d.** $\frac{6}{7} \times \frac{14}{15} = \frac{4}{5}$

5. **Change to a mixed number or whole number.** 2 each (8)

    a. $\frac{14}{7} = 2$ **b.** $\frac{25}{9} = 2\frac{7}{9}$ **c.** $\frac{7}{6} = 1\frac{1}{6}$ **d.** $\frac{81}{5} = 16\frac{1}{5}$

6. **Circle the proper fractions.** 2 each (16)

    ($\frac{1}{2}$) $\frac{5}{4}$ ($\frac{4}{5}$)   ($\frac{6}{7}$)   ($\frac{2}{9}$) $\frac{4}{3}$ ($\frac{3}{5}$) $\frac{13}{11}$

7. **Follow the directions.** 2 each (10)

    a. _____ $\frac{27}{5}$ _____ Change $5\frac{2}{5}$ to an improper fraction.

    b. _____ $\frac{6}{7}$ _____ Reduce $\frac{24}{28}$.

    c. _____ yes _____ Write yes if 342 is divisible by 9.

    d. _Answers will vary._ Write any mixed number.

    e. _____ 38 _____ Write the numerator of $\frac{38}{39}$.

Lesson 126　　3 min.

$14\frac{3}{4}$

$-6\frac{1}{2}$

$8\frac{1}{4}$

27

$-2\frac{5}{6}$

$24\frac{1}{6}$

$13\frac{1}{2}$

$-2\frac{2}{4}$

11

$7\frac{1}{3}$

$+2\frac{1}{6}$

$9\frac{1}{2}$

$3,721$
$\times\quad 6$
$22,326$

$5,297$
$\times\quad 6$
$31,782$

$8,706$
$\times\quad 5$
$43,530$

Lesson 128　　2 min.

×	4	11	8	2	9	10
12	48	132	96	24	108	120
8	32	88	64	16	72	80
6	24	66	48	12	54	60
3	12	33	24	6	27	30
9	36	99	72	18	81	90

Lesson 129　　3 min.

Average.

```
9 7        $ 5 3 . 2 6      1 3, 2 5 4
9 7        $ 1 8 . 3 2      7 8, 5 1 6
9 5        $ 4 9 . 7 8
9 3        $ 1 2 . 6 4      45,885
9 7
1 0 0         $33.50
96 r.3
```

Lesson 130　　5 min.

$8,329$
$-4,784$
$3,545$

$1,634$
$\times\quad 8$
$13,072$

$\$43.21$
-18.39
$\$24.82$

```
9 3          $ . 1 4
2 8            . 7 3
7 6            . 1 9
+ 3 7        + . 8 1
2 3 4        $ 1 . 8 7
```

$$33\text{ r. }4$$
$$7\overline{)235}$$

Quiz 10 each

Name _____

Lesson	Score
126	
128	
129	
130	

Quiz 13

Name _____ Date _____

1. Follow the signs. 5 each (20)

a.
$$\begin{array}{r} 3,209 \\ -1,372 \\ \hline 1,837 \end{array}$$

b.
$$\begin{array}{r} {\scriptstyle 6\,2} \\ 38 \\ +41 \\ \hline 141 \end{array}$$

c.
$$\begin{array}{r} 25\frac{1}{5} \\ +18\frac{1}{10} \\ \hline 43\frac{3}{10} \end{array}$$

d.
$$\begin{array}{r} 16\frac{3}{8} \\ -3\frac{2}{8} \\ \hline 13\frac{1}{8} \end{array}$$

2. Write the products. 5 each (15)

a. $\frac{2}{3} \times \frac{3}{4} = \underline{\frac{1}{2}}$

b. $\frac{3}{8} \times 6 = \underline{2\frac{1}{4}}$

c. $5 \times 2\frac{2}{5} = \underline{12}$

3. Add 7 to each number. Write only the sum on the blank below each number. 5 each (40)

50	24	38	72	16	49	93	57
57	31	45	79	23	56	100	64

4. Circle the four fractions that are in lowest terms. 5 each (20)

$\left(\frac{8}{9}\right)$ $\left(\frac{3}{4}\right)$ $\frac{6}{8}$ $\frac{2}{8}$ $\frac{5}{15}$ $\left(\frac{4}{9}\right)$ $\left(\frac{6}{11}\right)$ $\frac{3}{18}$

Lesson 131 — 1 min.

1 yard = __3__ feet

1 year = __12__ months

1 pound = __16__ ounces

1 meter = __1,000__ millimeters

1 gallon = __4__ quarts

1 bushel = __4__ pecks

I = __1__

V = __5__

X = __10__

L = __50__

C = __100__

D = __500__

M = __1,000__

Lesson 133 — 5 min.

$$
\begin{array}{r} 3 \\ \times 8 \\ \hline 2\,4 \end{array}
\qquad
\begin{array}{r} 6 \\ \times 9 \\ \hline 5\,4 \end{array}
\qquad
\begin{array}{r} 7 \\ \times 2 \\ \hline 1\,4 \end{array}
\qquad
\begin{array}{r} 8 \\ \times 8 \\ \hline 6\,4 \end{array}
\qquad
\begin{array}{r} 4 \\ \times 6 \\ \hline 2\,4 \end{array}
$$

$3\overline{)6}$ → 2 $2\overline{)8}$ → 4 $8\overline{)16}$ → 2 $5\overline{)40}$ → 8

$$
\begin{array}{r} 4 \\ + 5 \\ \hline 9 \end{array}
\qquad
\begin{array}{r} 6 \\ + 7 \\ \hline 1\,3 \end{array}
\qquad
\begin{array}{r} 3 \\ + 8 \\ \hline 1\,1 \end{array}
\qquad
\begin{array}{r} 2 \\ + 5 \\ \hline 7 \end{array}
\qquad
\begin{array}{r} 6 \\ + 6 \\ \hline 1\,2 \end{array}
$$

Quiz 5 each

Lesson 134 — 3 min.

24 pecks + 16 quarts = __26__ pecks

$$
\begin{array}{r} 9\,7.5 \\ 6\,8.3 \\ + 9\,9.4 \\ \hline 2\,6\,5.2 \end{array}
\qquad
\begin{array}{r} 6\,3.9 \\ - 4\,2.7 \\ \hline 2\,1.2 \end{array}
\qquad
\begin{array}{r} 7\,0.4 \\ - 1\,3.5 \\ \hline 5\,6.9 \end{array}
\qquad
\begin{array}{r} \$9.2\,4 \\ \times \quad 6 \\ \hline \$5\,5.4\,4 \end{array}
$$

Lesson 135 — 3 min.

$27\overline{)5,964}$ → 220 r.24

$83\overline{)7,421}$ → 89 r.34

$95\overline{)8,127}$ → 85 r.52

$14\overline{)3,801}$ → 271 r.7

Lesson	Score
131	
133	
134	
135	

Test 13

Grade [   ]

Name _____ Date _____

1. Match by putting the correct mixed decimal in each blank. 3 each (30)

a. __241.3__ two hundred forty-one and three tenths   64.17

b. __64.17__ sixty-four and seventeen hundredths   241.3

c. __90.1__ ninety and one tenth   3.08

d. __1,036.5__ one thousand thirty-six and five tenths   12.5

e. __28.05__ twenty-eight and five hundredths   1,036.5

f. __12.5__ $12\frac{5}{10}$ 28.05

g. __3.08__ $3\frac{8}{100}$ 16.1

h. __87.6__ $87\frac{6}{10}$ 87.6

i. __253.71__ $253\frac{71}{100}$ 90.1

j. __16.1__ $16\frac{1}{10}$ 253.71

2. Follow the signs. 2 each (10)

a.
$$5\frac{1}{3}$$
$$9$$
$$+\ 3\frac{1}{6}$$
$$\overline{17\frac{1}{2}}$$

b.
$$7\,3\frac{2}{5}$$
$$-\ 5\,8\frac{1}{2}$$
$$\overline{1\,4\frac{9}{10}}$$

c.
$$9,2\,0\,7$$
$$-\ 2,0\,0\,9$$
$$\overline{7,1\,9\,8}$$

d.
$$6\,4$$
$$5\,2$$
$$+\ 4\,8$$
$$\overline{1\,6\,4}$$

e.
$$3\,8\frac{7}{8}$$
$$-\ 1\,2\frac{3}{8}$$
$$\overline{2\,6\frac{1}{2}}$$

3. Divide and check. 2 each part (12)

a. $24\overline{)2,099}$ 87 r. 11

$$87$$
$$\times\,24$$
$$\overline{2,088}$$
$$+\quad 11$$
$$\overline{2,099}$$

b. $33\overline{)3,009}$ 91 r. 6

$$91$$
$$\times\,33$$
$$\overline{3,003}$$
$$+\quad 6$$
$$\overline{3,009}$$

c. $46\overline{)1,297}$ 28 r. 9

$$28$$
$$\times\,46$$
$$\overline{1,288}$$
$$+\quad 9$$
$$\overline{1,297}$$

lesson 132   **105**

4. Find the products. 2 each (6)

   a. $\frac{2}{5} \times \frac{1}{3} = \frac{2}{15}$ **b.** $4 \times 3\frac{1}{2} = 14$ **c.** $4\frac{2}{5} \times 15 = 66$

5. Answer these questions about this number: 1,527.83. 2 each (12)

   a. _____5_____ What digit is in the hundreds' place?

   b. _____7_____ What digit is in the ones' place?

   c. _____8_____ What digit is in the tenths' place?

   d. _____1_____ What digit is in the thousands' place?

   e. _____2_____ What digit is in the tens' place?

   f. _____3_____ What digit is in the hundredths' place?

6. Fill in the blanks. 2 each (24)

   a. 1 mile = _5,280_ feet   **b.** 1 leap year = _366_ days

   c. 1 day = _24_ hours   **d.** 1 peck = _8_ quarts

   e. 1 century = _100_ years   **f.** 1 pound = _16_ ounces

   g. deci = $\frac{1}{10}$ or .1   **h.** deca = _10_

   i. hecto = _100_   **j.** milli = $\frac{1}{1,000}$ or .001

   k. kilo = _1,000_   **l.** centi = $\frac{1}{100}$ or .01

7. Write *true* or *false* in each blank. 1 each (4)

   a. _____true_____ A decimal is another way to write a fraction.

   b. _____true_____ $\frac{7}{10} = .7$

   c. _____true_____ 7.32 is a mixed decimal.

   d. _____false_____ $\frac{1}{2} \times 56 = 23$

+	18	41	27	5	19	16
3	21	44	30	8	22	19
7	25	48	34	12	26	23
2	20	43	29	7	21	18
9	27	50	36	14	28	25
8	26	49	35	13	27	24

$$\begin{array}{r} 1 \\ -\ \frac{3}{5} \\ \hline \frac{2}{5} \end{array} \qquad \begin{array}{r} 1\,4 \\ -\ 6\frac{2}{9} \\ \hline 7\frac{7}{9} \end{array}$$

$$\begin{array}{r} 1\,1\frac{1}{2} \\ -\ 6\frac{2}{4} \\ \hline 5 \end{array} \qquad \begin{array}{r} \frac{9}{11} \\ +\ \frac{1}{11} \\ \hline \frac{10}{11} \end{array}$$

$$\begin{array}{r} \frac{3}{10} \\ +\ \frac{2}{10} \\ \hline \frac{1}{2} \end{array} \qquad \begin{array}{r} 3\,9\frac{1}{5} \\ +\ 1\,7\frac{3}{10} \\ \hline 5\,6\frac{1}{2} \end{array}$$

Quiz 10 each

$$\begin{array}{r} 27.06 \\ 83.59 \\ +\ 51.38 \\ \hline 162.03 \end{array} \quad \begin{array}{r} 16.3 \\ 8.9 \\ +\ 29.7 \\ \hline 54.9 \end{array} \quad \begin{array}{r} 632.81 \\ 47.09 \\ +\ 599.20 \\ \hline 1,279.10 \end{array}$$

$$\begin{array}{r} \$56.38 \\ \times\ \ 24 \\ \hline \$1,353.12 \end{array} \quad \begin{array}{r} \$97.82 \\ \times\ \ 9 \\ \hline \$880.38 \end{array} \quad \begin{array}{r} \$15.39 \\ \times\ \ 27 \\ \hline \$415.53 \end{array}$$

×	9	6	8	12	3	7
11	99	66	88	132	33	77
5	45	30	40	60	15	35
12	108	72	96	144	36	84
10	90	60	80	120	30	70
0	0	0	0	0	0	0

Name _____

Lesson	Score
136	
138	
139	
140	

Quiz 14

Name _____ Date _____

1. Follow the signs. 5 each (50)

a.
```
  3 2 4
  8 9 5
  6 1 7
+ 4 0 9
-------
2, 2 4 5
```

b.
```
  2, 3 0 4
- 1, 5 0 9
---------
      7 9 5
```

c.
```
  2 9. 4
  8 7. 6
+ 2 3. 1
-------
1 4 0. 1
```

d.
```
  1 6. 3 5
-  9. 0 9
--------
   7. 2 6
```

e. $\frac{2}{5} \times \frac{5}{6} = \underline{\frac{1}{3}}$

f. $\frac{5}{14} \times \frac{7}{10} = \underline{\frac{1}{4}}$

g. $\frac{4}{5} \times \frac{5}{8} = \underline{\frac{1}{2}}$

h.
$$
\begin{array}{r}
1 \\
- \frac{3}{4} \\
\hline
\frac{1}{4}
\end{array}
$$

i.
$$
\begin{array}{r}
8 \frac{1}{4} \\
+ 5 \frac{1}{4} \\
\hline
1 3 \frac{1}{2}
\end{array}
$$

j.
```
  1. 6 7
-  . 5 9
-------
  1. 0 8
```

2. Write the fractions as decimals. 5 each (20)

a. $\frac{3}{10} = \underline{.3}$

b. $\frac{31}{100} = \underline{.31}$

c. $\frac{3}{100} = \underline{.03}$

d. $\frac{421}{1,000} = \underline{.421}$

3. Circle the four proper fractions. 5 each (20)

$\boxed{\frac{2}{9}}$ $\boxed{\frac{3}{7}}$ $\frac{11}{3}$ $\boxed{\frac{8}{9}}$ $\frac{3}{2}$ $\boxed{\frac{4}{11}}$

4. Multiply each number by 9. 2 each (10)

| 7 _63_ | 12 _108_ | 5 _45_ | 11 _99_ | 8 _72_ |

Lesson 141   2 min.

Write as decimals.

$\frac{4}{10}$ = .4 $\frac{5}{10}$ = .5 $\frac{3}{10}$ = .3

$\frac{8}{10}$ = .8 $\frac{14}{100}$ = .14 $\frac{23}{100}$ = .23

$\frac{17}{100}$ = .17 $\frac{3}{100}$ = .03 $\frac{201}{1,000}$ = .201

$\frac{67}{1,000}$ = .067 $\frac{387}{1,000}$ = .387 $\frac{5}{1,000}$ = .005

Lesson 143   2 min.

×	11	9	12	2	5	7
10	110	90	120	20	50	70
12	132	108	144	24	60	84
5	55	45	60	10	25	35
9	99	81	108	18	45	63
8	88	72	96	16	40	56

Lesson 144   5 min.

÷	108	72	81	63	45	9	54
9	12	8	9	7	5	1	6

×	8	12	5	9	11	10	7
12	96	144	60	108	132	120	84

Lesson 145   2 min.

Reduce.

$\frac{7}{14}$ = $\frac{1}{2}$ $\frac{3}{15}$ = $\frac{1}{5}$ $\frac{6}{12}$ = $\frac{1}{2}$

$\frac{4}{8}$ = $\frac{1}{2}$ $\frac{2}{10}$ = $\frac{1}{5}$ $\frac{6}{10}$ = $\frac{3}{5}$

$50 \div 2 \div 5 \times 6 \div 3 =$ __10__

$56 \div 7 \div 4 \div 2 \times 0 =$ __0__

$\frac{1}{9}$ of 81 = __9__ $\frac{3}{7}$ = $\frac{9}{21}$

$\frac{1}{7}$ of 49 = __7__ $\frac{5}{9}$ = $\frac{20}{36}$

$\frac{1}{8}$ of 64 = __8__ $\frac{4}{11}$ = $\frac{24}{66}$

Lesson	Score
141	
143	
144	
145	

Test 14

Name _____ Date _____

1. Write each mixed number or fraction as a decimal. 2 each (10)

    a. $\frac{3}{10}$ = ___.3___   **b.** $\frac{65}{100}$ = ___.65___   **c.** $12\frac{5}{10}$ = ___12.5___

    d. $705\frac{17}{100}$ = ___705.17___   **e.** $92\frac{6}{100}$ = ___92.06___

2. Write as a mixed number or fraction. 2 each (10)

    a. 4.7 = ___$4\frac{7}{10}$___   **b.** .77 = ___$\frac{77}{100}$___   **c.** 8.03 = ___$8\frac{3}{100}$___

    d. 27.13 = ___$27\frac{13}{100}$___   **e.** 1.61 = ___$1\frac{61}{100}$___

3. Read these words carefully and write the number on the line. 2 each (10)

    a. ___65.15___ Sixty-five and fifteen hundredths

    b. ___153.2___ One hundred fifty-three and two tenths

    c. ___31,691___ Thirty-one thousand six hundred ninety-one

    d. ___$15.78___ Fifteen dollars and seventy-eight cents

    e. ___$319.25___ Three hundred nineteen dollars and twenty-five cents

4. Follow the signs. 3 each (15)

    a.
$$17\frac{3}{8}$$
$$-\ 6\frac{3}{4}$$
$$\overline{10\frac{5}{8}}$$

    b.
$$8,465$$
$$\times\ \ \ \ 36$$
$$\overline{304,740}$$

    c.
$$6.17$$
$$11.80$$
$$+\ 7.66$$
$$\overline{25.63}$$

    d.
$$\frac{3}{5}$$
$$\frac{1}{3}$$
$$+\ \frac{1}{6}$$
$$\overline{1\frac{1}{10}}$$

    e.
$$8.00$$
$$-\ 6.32$$
$$\overline{1.68}$$

By doing nothing, men learn to do evil. —Columella

5. Divide and check. 2 each part (12)

a. $36\overline{)18,972}$ $\dfrac{527}{}$

$$\begin{array}{r} 527 \\ \times\,36 \\ \hline 18,972 \end{array}$$

b. $19\overline{)13,058}$ $687\ r.\ 5$

$$\begin{array}{r} 687 \\ \times\,19 \\ \hline 13,053 \\ +\quad 5 \\ \hline 13,058 \end{array}$$

c. $41\overline{)34,768}$ 848

$$\begin{array}{r} 848 \\ \times\,41 \\ \hline 34,768 \end{array}$$

6. Measure these lines to the nearest one half inch with your ruler. Write the lengths on the blanks at the left. 2 each (10)

a. _____1 inch_____

b. _____$2\frac{1}{2}$ inches_____

c. _____4 inches_____

d. _____2 inches_____

e. _____$3\frac{1}{2}$ inches_____

7. Use the words or numbers in the box to fill in the blanks. 3 each (18)

| $\frac{1}{100}$ | grams | 1,000 | meters | $\frac{1}{10}$ | liters | 100 |

a. The metric system uses _____meters_____ to measure length.

b. The prefix kilo means _____1,000_____.

c. The prefix centi means _____$\frac{1}{100}$_____.

d. The metric system uses _____liters_____ to measure liquids.

e. The prefix deci means _____$\frac{1}{10}$_____.

f. The prefix hecto means _____100_____.

8. Find the products. 4 each (12)

a. $\frac{3}{4} \times \frac{2}{6} = \frac{1}{4}$

b. $4\frac{2}{5} \times 25 = 110$

c. $16 \times 12\frac{1}{4} = 196$

114

Arithmetic 4

Match.

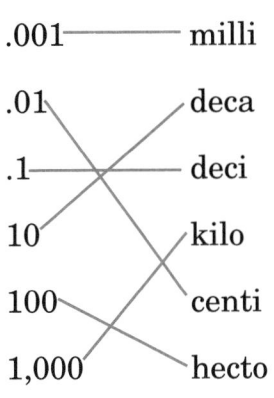

.001 ——— milli

.01 deca

.1 deci

10 kilo

100 centi

1,000 hecto

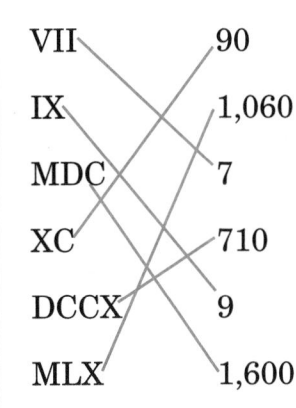

VII 90

IX 1,060

MDC 7

XC 710

DCCX 9

MLX 1,600

$1 = \frac{6}{6}$ $1 = \frac{9}{9}$ $1 = \frac{5}{5}$ $1 = \frac{4}{4}$

| $\begin{array}{r}7\,2 \\ \times\,6 \\ \hline 4\,3\,2\end{array}$ | $\begin{array}{r}5\,8 \\ \times\,9 \\ \hline 5\,2\,2\end{array}$ | $\begin{array}{r}4\,7 \\ \times\,5 \\ \hline 2\,3\,5\end{array}$ | $\begin{array}{r}2\,3 \\ \times\,4 \\ \hline 9\,2\end{array}$ |

| $\begin{array}{r}9\,4 \\ \times\,9 \\ \hline 8\,4\,6\end{array}$ | $\begin{array}{r}7\,1 \\ \times\,8 \\ \hline 5\,6\,8\end{array}$ | $\begin{array}{r}5\,4 \\ \times\,6 \\ \hline 3\,2\,4\end{array}$ | $\begin{array}{r}9\,3 \\ \times\,4 \\ \hline 3\,7\,2\end{array}$ |

| $\begin{array}{r}4\,7 \\ \times\,6 \\ \hline 2\,8\,2\end{array}$ | $\begin{array}{r}5\,4 \\ \times\,9 \\ \hline 4\,8\,6\end{array}$ | $\begin{array}{r}9\,7 \\ \times\,8 \\ \hline 7\,7\,6\end{array}$ | $\begin{array}{r}2\,6 \\ \times\,3 \\ \hline 7\,8\end{array}$ |

Quiz 5 each

+	3	11	9	10	7	8
27	30	38	36	37	34	35
36	39	47	45	46	43	44
19	22	30	28	29	26	27
8	11	19	17	18	15	16
41	44	52	50	51	48	49

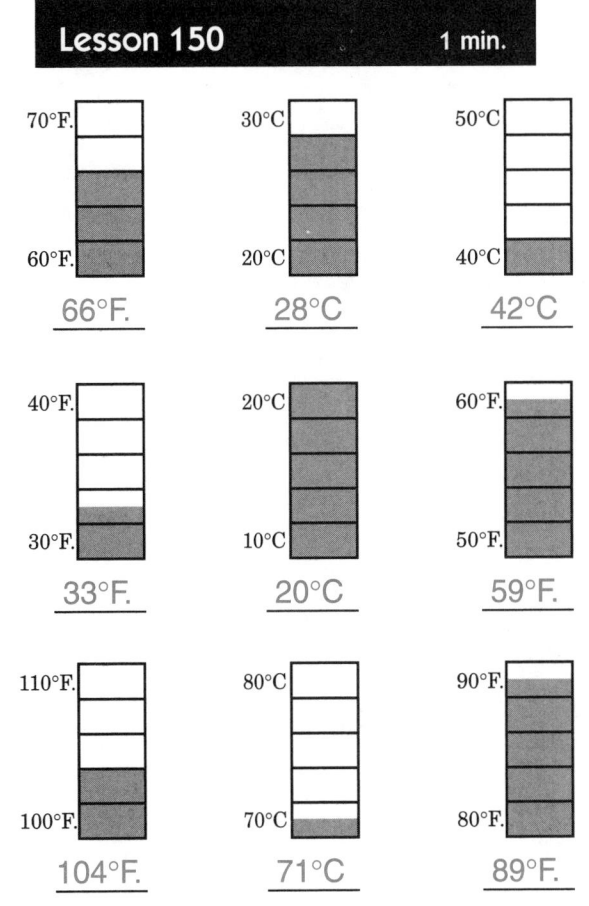

66°F.   28°C   42°C

33°F.   20°C   59°F.

104°F.   71°C   89°F.

Lesson	Score
146	
148	
149	
150	

Quiz 15

Name _____ Date _____

1. Match by putting the correct numbers in the blanks. 3 each (24)

a. __2__ used to measure length

b. __7__ used to measure capacity

c. __1__ deci

d. __6__ kilo

e. __4__ centi

f. __5__ deca

g. __3__ milli

h. __8__ hecto

1. $\frac{1}{10}$
2. meter
3. $\frac{1}{1,000}$
4. $\frac{1}{100}$
5. 10
6. 1,000
7. liter
8. 100

2. Choose the correct answer and write it in the blank. 5 each (30)

a. The fraction $\frac{1}{10}$ can also be written as the decimal __.1__. (.1 or .01)

b. The fraction $\frac{1}{1,000}$ can also be written as the decimal __.001__. (.001 or .01)

c. The fraction $\frac{1}{100}$ can also be written as the decimal __.01__. (.01 or .001)

d. There are __1,000__ meters in a kilometer. (10 or 1,000)

e. There are __100__ meters in a hectometer. (100 or 10)

f. There are __10__ meters in a decameter. (10 or 100)

3. Write the correct temperature in the blank. 5 each (20)

a.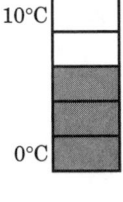

__6°C__

b.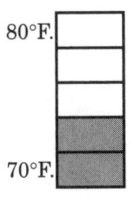

__74°F.__

c.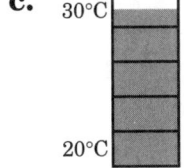

__29°C__

d.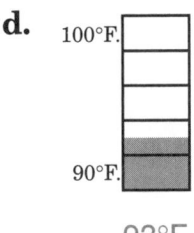

__93°F.__

4. Subtract 7 from each number. Write only the differences on the lines.
4 each (24)

51	69	85	44	22	96
44	62	78	37	15	89

Solve and check.

$x + 3 = 9 \times 4$
    x = 33

$y - 5 = 16 \div 8$
    y = 7

$x - 2 = 4 \times 4$
    x = 18

$g + 5 = 17 - 6$
    g = 6

×	11	9	7	10	6	12
7	77	63	49	70	42	84
8	88	72	56	80	48	96
10	110	90	70	100	60	120
9	99	81	63	90	54	108
6	66	54	42	60	36	72

$$\begin{array}{r} 6,257 \text{ r. }8 \\ 9\overline{)56,321} \end{array}$$

$$\begin{array}{r} 1,834 \\ 8\overline{)14,672} \end{array}$$

$$\begin{array}{r} 24 \text{ r. }3 \\ 24\overline{)579} \end{array}$$

$$\begin{array}{r} 14 \text{ r. }28 \\ 52\overline{)756} \end{array}$$

Write the Roman numerals from 1 to 20.

  I   II   III   IV   V

  VI   VII   VIII   IX   X

  XI   XII   XIII   XIV   XV

  XVI   XVII   XVIII   XIX   XX

Quiz 5 each

Name _____

Lesson	Score
151	
153	
154	
155	

Arithmetic 4

Test 15

Name _____ Date _____

1. Read each statement carefully and fill in the blanks with the correct prefixes. Cross out each prefix as you use it. 3 each (18)

> deci   centi   milli   deca   hecto   kilo

a. A __deca__ liter equals 10 liters.   **b.** A __centi__ meter equals $\frac{1}{100}$ of a meter.

c. A __kilo__ gram equals 1,000 grams.   **d.** A __deci__ meter equals $\frac{1}{10}$ of a meter.

e. A __hecto__ liter equals 100 liters.   **f.** A __milli__ gram equals $\frac{1}{1,000}$ of a gram.

2. Solve and check these equations. 2 each (6)

a. $n + 6 = 5 + 2$
    $n = 1$

b. $x + 3 = 14 - 6$
    $x = 5$

c. $b - 8 = 5 \times 2$
    $b = 18$

3. Divide and check. 2 each part (12)

a. $48\overline{)7{,}632}$ → 159
$$\begin{array}{r} 159 \\ \times\,48 \\ \hline 7{,}632 \end{array}$$

b. $17\overline{)6{,}570}$ → 386 r. 8
$$\begin{array}{r} 386 \\ \times\,17 \\ \hline 6{,}562 \\ +\quad 8 \\ \hline 6{,}570 \end{array}$$

c. $79\overline{)52{,}973}$ → 670 r. 43
$$\begin{array}{r} 670 \\ \times\,79 \\ \hline 52{,}930 \\ +\quad 43 \\ \hline 52{,}973 \end{array}$$

4. Fill in the blanks with *meter, liter, gram,* or *Celsius*. Some answers will be used twice. 2 each (12)

a. A _____liter_____ is used to measure capacity.

b. A _____meter_____ is used to measure length.

c. To weigh a can of pepper, use _____gram_____.

d. To measure how much milk, use _____liter_____.

e. To measure the length of a room, use _____meter_____.

f. To measure temperature in metric units, use _____Celsius_____.

Whatsoever thy hand findeth to do, do it with thy might.

—Ecc. 9:10

5. Follow the signs. 3 each (15)

a.
$$
\begin{array}{r}
6,000.0 \\
-\,3,139.2 \\
\hline
2,860.8
\end{array}
$$

b.
$$
\begin{array}{r}
847.1 \\
171.4 \\
+\,623.7 \\
\hline
1,642.2
\end{array}
$$

c.
$$
\begin{array}{r}
362 \\
\times\,186 \\
\hline
67,332
\end{array}
$$

d.
$$
\begin{array}{r}
31\frac{8}{9} \\
97\frac{2}{3} \\
+\,53 \\
\hline
182\frac{5}{9}
\end{array}
$$

e.
$$
\begin{array}{r}
57\frac{5}{10} \\
-\,49\frac{1}{2} \\
\hline
8
\end{array}
$$

6. Change to a mixed number. 1 each (4)

a. $23.3 = \underline{23\frac{3}{10}}$ **b.** $16.09 = \underline{16\frac{9}{100}}$ **c.** $19.17 = \underline{19\frac{17}{100}}$ **d.** $5.871 = \underline{5\frac{871}{1,000}}$

7. Write the products. 1 each (13)

×	4	7	12	1	10	11	0	3	2	9	6	8	5
9	36	63	108	9	90	99	0	27	18	81	54	72	45

8. Multiply. 2 each (8)

a. $\frac{5}{7} \times \frac{3}{5} = \frac{3}{7}$ **b.** $1\frac{1}{5} \times \frac{5}{6} = 1$ **c.** $10 \times \frac{1}{2} = 5$ **d.** $\frac{5}{8} \times \frac{4}{7} = \frac{5}{14}$

9. Write the correct letter in the blank. 2 each (10)

___c___	△
___e___	
___d___	
___a___	
___b___	•

a. parallel lines

b. point

c. triangle

d. quadrilateral

e. line

Lesson 156 — 3 min.

Average.

5 9	$ 5 2 . 0 8	1 1
7 6	$ 6 7 . 3 2	9
5 7	$ 5 8 . 1 4	1 5
9 2	$59.18	8
7 6		6
72		9 r.4

Lesson 158 — 2 min. 30 sec.

$$\frac{3}{8} \times \frac{4}{7} = \frac{3}{14} \qquad \frac{5}{6} \times \frac{3}{5} = \frac{1}{2} \qquad 1\frac{1}{2} \times \frac{4}{5} = 1\frac{1}{5}$$

$$12 \times \frac{1}{2} = 6 \qquad \frac{3}{8} \times 12 = 4\frac{1}{2} \qquad \frac{4}{7} \times 1\frac{3}{4} = 1$$

Lesson 159 — 5 min.

Solve and check.

$n + 6 = 8 \times 2$
$n = 10$

$y - 4 = 36 \div 9$
$y = 8$

$e + 4 = 16 - 9$
$e = 3$

$n + 5 = 6 \times 5$
$n = 25$

Lesson 160 — 2 min.

×	10	12	2	5	9	0
11	110	132	22	55	99	0
8	80	96	16	40	72	0
5	50	60	10	25	45	0
6	60	72	12	30	54	0
9	90	108	18	45	81	0

Quiz 15 each

123

Lesson	Score
156	
158	
159	
160	

Quiz 16

Name _____ Date _____

1. Identify. 3 each (30)

a.  b. 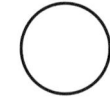 c. 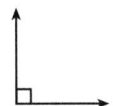 d.  e. ⟵⟶

<u>triangle</u> <u>circle</u> <u>right angle</u> <u>trapezoid</u> <u>line</u>

f. • g. ⟷⟷ h. 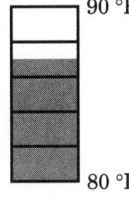 i. •—• j. •—⟶

<u>point</u> <u>parallel lines</u> <u>parallelogram</u> <u>line segment</u> <u>ray</u>

2. Write the correct temperatures. 5 each (20)

a. 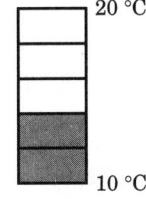 90 °F. / 80 °F. b. 20 °C / 10 °C c. 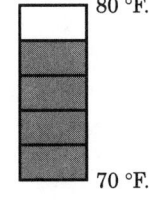 80 °F. / 70 °F. d. 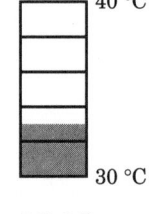 40 °C / 30 °C

<u>87 °F.</u>   <u>14 °C</u>   <u>78 °F.</u>   <u>33 °C</u>

3. Change to a mixed number. 5 each (20)

a. $\frac{9}{4} =$ <u>$2\frac{1}{4}$</u>   b. $\frac{18}{5} =$ <u>$3\frac{3}{5}$</u>   c. $\frac{27}{4} =$ <u>$6\frac{3}{4}$</u>   d. $\frac{19}{3} =$ <u>$6\frac{1}{3}$</u>

4. Follow the signs. 5 each (25)

a.
```
  8 7.9 5
  3 8.7 6
  2 9.9 4
+ 1 2.7 3
─────────
1 6 9.3 8
```

b.
```
  $ 2 8.9 5
×       3 4
───────────
  1 1 5 8 0
+ 8 6 8 5
───────────
  $ 9 8 4.3 0
```

c.
```
  3,8 7 9.5
− 2,3 9 8.7
───────────
  1,4 8 0.8
```

d.
```
  6 7.1
  2 9.5
  4 4.3
+ 3 8.0
───────
1 7 8.9
```

e.
```
  $ 7.9 5
×       9
─────────
  $ 7 1.5 5
```

Lesson 161 — 3 min.

Find the areas of these rectangles.

$l = 5$ ft.
$w = 3$ ft.
$A = 15$ sq. ft.

$l = 9$ ft.
$w = 7$ ft.
$A = 63$ sq. ft.

$l = 30$ in.
$w = 12$ in.
$A = 360$ sq. in.

$l = 8$ ft.
$w = 5$ ft.
$A = 40$ sq. ft.

Lesson 163 — 1 min. 30 sec.

×	11	5	0	8	4	2
9	99	45	0	72	36	18
12	132	60	0	96	48	24
8	88	40	0	64	32	16
6	66	30	0	48	24	12
7	77	35	0	56	28	14

Lesson 164 — 5 min.

$$
\begin{array}{r} 87 \\ \times\,9 \\ \hline 783 \end{array}
\quad
\begin{array}{r} 56 \\ \times\,7 \\ \hline 392 \end{array}
\quad
\begin{array}{r} 49 \\ \times\,6 \\ \hline 294 \end{array}
\quad
\begin{array}{r} 28 \\ \times\,3 \\ \hline 84 \end{array}
\quad
\begin{array}{r} 16 \\ \times\,9 \\ \hline 144 \end{array}
$$

$\frac{1}{3}$ of 12 = ___4___ $\frac{1}{5}$ of 10 = ___2___

$$
\begin{array}{r} 92 \\ \times\,8 \\ \hline 736 \end{array}
\quad
\begin{array}{r} 66 \\ \times\,3 \\ \hline 198 \end{array}
\quad
\begin{array}{r} 47 \\ \times\,9 \\ \hline 423 \end{array}
\quad
\begin{array}{r} 16 \\ \times\,5 \\ \hline 80 \end{array}
\quad
\begin{array}{r} 35 \\ \times\,9 \\ \hline 315 \end{array}
$$

$6\overline{)24}$ → 4 $7\overline{)35}$ → 5 $4\overline{)20}$ → 5 $9\overline{)36}$ → 4

Lesson 165 — 3 min.

Find the areas of these rectangles.

$l = 14$ yd.
$w = 8$ yd.
$A = 112$ sq. yd.

$l = 36$ in.
$w = 24$ in.
$A = 864$ sq. in.

Find the perimeters of these rectangles.

$l = 14$ yd.
$w = 8$ yd.
$P = 44$ yd.

$l = 36$ in.
$w = 24$ in.
$P = 120$ in.

Quiz 5 each

Lesson	Score
161	
163	
164	
165	

Test 16

Name _____ Date _____

1. Fill in the blanks. Use the words in the box. 2 each (6)

> right   multiply   square

a. To find the area of a rectangle, _____multiply_____ its length by its width.

b. A square, one inch by one inch, is called one _____square_____ inch.

c. A rectangle and a square have four corners or _____right_____ angles.

2. Find the perimeters of these rectangles.
Use the formula $P = (2 \times l) + (2 \times w)$. 2 each (12)

a. 4 ft. by 5 ft.

   18 ft.

b. 5 in. by 6 in.

   22 in.

c. 8 in. by 10 in.

   36 in.

d. 15 yd. by 19 yd.

   68 yd.

e. 4 yd. by 7 yd.

   22 yd.

f. 7 ft. by 16 ft.

   46 ft.

3. Subtract. 3 each (15)

a.
```
  683
- 293
-----
  390
```

b.
```
  501
- 126
-----
  375
```

c.
```
 9,667
-  792
------
 8,875
```

d.
```
 $68.15
- 64.26
-------
  $3.89
```

e.
```
 3,700.0
-2,243.7
--------
 1,456.3
```

4. Divide and check. 2 each part (12)

a.
```
      20
37)740      20
           ×37
          ----
           740
```

b.
```
      155
40)6,200    155
            ×40
           -----
           6,200
```

c.
```
      80 r.32
69)5,552     80
            ×69
           -----
           5,520
           +  32
           -----
           5,552
```

Good is not good, where better is expected. —Thomas Fuller

5. Match by putting the correct number in the blank. Choose the unit you would use to measure these things. 2 each (10)

a. __4__ weight of a car
b. __5__ length of a room
c. __2__ weight of a letter
d. __3__ time of a speed test
e. __1__ amount of gasoline bought

1. gallons or liters
2. ounces or grams
3. minutes
4. tons or metric tons
5. feet or meters

6. Follow the signs. 3 each (15)

a.
$$\begin{array}{r} 3.05 \\ 2.40 \\ 4.48 \\ 2.16 \\ +\ 3.95 \\ \hline 16.04 \end{array}$$

b.
$$\begin{array}{r} 16\frac{1}{2} \\ 32 \\ +\ 21\frac{3}{4} \\ \hline 70\frac{1}{4} \end{array}$$

c.
$$\begin{array}{r} 1{,}723 \\ \times\ \ \ 5 \\ \hline 8{,}615 \end{array}$$

d.
$$\begin{array}{r} 892 \\ \times\ 24 \\ \hline 21{,}408 \end{array}$$

e.
$$\begin{array}{r} 19\frac{1}{10} \\ -\ 3\frac{5}{20} \\ \hline 15\frac{17}{20} \end{array}$$

7. Solve the multiplication block. 2 each (26)

×	3	9	12	1	2	0	7	10	5	11	6	8	4
12	36	108	144	12	24	0	84	120	60	132	72	96	48

8. Multiply. 1 each (4)

a. $\frac{3}{11} \times \frac{2}{3} = \frac{2}{11}$
b. $1\frac{1}{5} \times \frac{3}{8} = \frac{9}{20}$
c. $12 \times \frac{4}{7} = 6\frac{6}{7}$
d. $\frac{6}{7} \times \frac{14}{15} = \frac{4}{5}$

130   Arithmetic 4

Lesson 166 — 3 min.

×	10	9	12	4	8	11
11	110	99	132	44	88	121
7	70	63	84	28	56	77
6	60	54	72	24	48	66
12	120	108	144	48	96	132
2	20	18	24	8	16	22

Quiz 3 each

Lesson 167 — 4 min.

$$678 \times 424 = 287,472$$

$$307 \times 452 = 138,764$$

$$975 \times 462 = 450,450$$

$$63\overline{)84,029} = 1,333 \text{ r.} 50$$

$$27\overline{)567} = 21$$

Lesson 168 — 2 min.

Find the area of each rectangle.

$l = 9$ ft.
$w = 7$ ft.
$A = 63$ sq. ft.

$l = 14$ in.
$w = 12$ in.
$A = 168$ sq. in.

$l = 19$ ft.
$w = 3$ ft.
$A = 57$ sq. ft.

$l = 27$ in.
$w = 8$ in.
$A = 216$ sq. in.

Lesson 169 — 2 min.

×	3	7	9	6	11	8
7	21	49	63	42	77	56
9	27	63	81	54	99	72
5	15	35	45	30	55	40
12	36	84	108	72	132	96
6	18	42	54	36	66	48
4	12	28	36	24	44	32
8	24	56	72	48	88	64

Lesson	Score
166	
167	
168	
169	

Arithmetic 4

Final Exam

Grade ☐

Name _____ Date _____

1. Match each section by placing the correct letter in the blank. 1 each (20)

———————————————— **Section 1** ————————————————

____c____ point

____a____ ray

____d____ line segment

____e____ line

____b____ angle

a.

b.

c.

d.

e.

———————————————— **Section 2** ————————————————

____b____ $l \times w$

____d____ $s \times s$

____a____ $(2 \times l) + (2 \times w)$

____c____ $4 \times s$

a. perimeter of a rectangle

b. area of a rectangle

c. perimeter of a square

d. area of a square

———————————————— **Section 3** ————————————————

____e____ two hundredths

____c____ two thousandths

____a____ two tenths

____d____ twenty-two thousandths

____b____ twenty-two hundredths

a. .2

b. .22

c. .002

d. .022

e. .02

———————————————— **Section 4** ————————————————

____e____ hecto

____a____ milli

____f____ kilo

____c____ deci

____d____ deca

____b____ centi

a. .001

b. .01

c. .1

d. 10

e. 100

f. 1,000

2. Follow the directions. 1 each (7)

a. _____22_____ Write the Arabic numeral for XXII.

b. _____144_____ Write the number of square inches in a square foot.

c. _____9_____ Write the number of square feet in a square yard.

d. _____72_____ Multiply 12 by 6.

e. _____$1\frac{3}{5}$_____ Change $\frac{8}{5}$ to a mixed number.

f. _____$\frac{1}{2}$_____ Reduce $\frac{4}{8}$ to lowest terms.

g. _____.7_____ Write $\frac{7}{10}$ as a decimal.

3. Follow the signs. 2 each (24)

a.
$$6\frac{1}{4}$$
$$+\,2\frac{1}{2}$$
$$8\frac{3}{4}$$

b.
$$\$65.89$$
$$-\,27.90$$
$$\$37.99$$

c.
$$8\frac{1}{2}$$
$$-\,5\frac{3}{16}$$
$$3\frac{5}{16}$$

d.
$$\$70.97$$
$$\times\qquad 8$$
$$\$567.76$$

e. $\frac{3}{5} \times 30 =$ _____18_____

f. $\frac{1}{4} \times \frac{2}{5} =$ _____$\frac{1}{10}$_____

g.
$$597$$
$$\times\,25$$
$$14,925$$

h. $5 \times 4\frac{2}{5} =$ _____22_____

i.
$$765.5$$
$$+\,128.4$$
$$893.9$$

j.
$$\frac{2}{3}$$
$$+\,\frac{1}{4}$$
$$\frac{11}{12}$$

k. $\frac{5}{8} \times \frac{4}{15} =$ _____$\frac{1}{6}$_____

l.
$$9\frac{1}{8}$$
$$-\,4\frac{3}{4}$$
$$4\frac{3}{8}$$

Name _____

4. Draw and label a square and a trapezoid. 2 each (4)

5. Solve and check this equation. 2

$$n + 6 = 27 - 9$$
$$n = 12$$

a. ____square____ **b.** ____trapezoid____

6. Divide and check. Write the remainder in c as a fraction. 1 each part (6)

a.
```
        9 4 6
    9 | 8,5 1 4      9 4 6
                   ×     9
                   8,5 1 4
```

b.
```
       1 2 r. 3 1
   5 1 | 6 4 3       1 2
                  × 5 1
                  6 1 2
                  + 3 1
                  6 4 3
```

c.
```
        5 3 ⅕
   3 5 | 1,8 6 2      5 3
                   × 3 5
                   1,8 5 5
                   +    7
                   1,8 6 2
```

7. Look at these fractions. They need to be either changed or reduced. Decide which needs to be done and do it. 2 each (6)

a. $\frac{16}{24} =$ ____$\frac{2}{3}$____   **b.** $\frac{15}{3} =$ ____5____   **c.** $\frac{7}{28} =$ ____$\frac{1}{4}$____

8. Find the area. 2 each (6)

a. *rectangle*
9 ft. by 14 ft.
$A = 126$ sq. ft.

b. *rectangle*
$l = 8$ ft.; $w = 5$ ft.
$A = 40$ sq. ft.

c. *square*
$s = 9$ in.
$A = 81$ sq. in.

I have fought a good fight, I have finished
my course, I have kept the faith. —2 Tim. 4:7

9. Find the perimeter. 2 each (6)

a. *rectangle*
9 in. by 16 in.

$P = 50$ in.

b. *square*
$s = 6$ yd.

$P = 24$ yd.

c. *rectangle*
$l = 13$ ft.; $w = 7$ ft.

$P = 40$ ft.

10. Write the temperature. 2

a.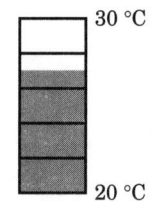

27 °C

11. Write the products. 1 each (8)

×	5	12	8	6
7	35	84	56	42
9	45	108	72	54

12. Write the answers. 1 each (9)

a. 1 ft. = __12__ in.

b. 1 yr. = __365__ da.

c. 1 hr. = __60__ min.

d. 1 bu. = __4__ pk.

e. 1 qt. = __2__ pt.

f. 1 m = __100__ cm

g. 1 mi. = __5,280__ ft.

h. 1 lb. = __16__ oz.

i. 1 kg = __1,000__ g